Wild Flowers
of Britain and Europe

JACQUES de SLOOVER
and MARTINE GOOSSENS

Translated by Dr Lucia Woodward and
edited by Dr Paul Sterry

David & Charles

CONTENTS

Preface   3
How to use this guide   5
  General notes   5
  The meaning of the symbols   7
Introduction to the use of herbs   14
  Active agents and drugs   14
  Natural characteristics of the active principles 15
  The plant organs most commonly used   19
  Should herbs be gathered or cultivated?   20
  Preparation, drying and storage of herbs   22
THE FIELD GUIDE
Appendix I   Botanical notes   169
Appendix II   Herbs and health   183
      How to prepare and use the plants   183
      Glossary of therapeutic properties   185
      Alphabetical table of ailments and treatments 191
Appendix III   Herbs in the kitchen   197
Glossary of botanical terminology   199
Further reading   203
Index   207

A DAVID & CHARLES BOOK

First published in Italy by Priuli et Verlucca editori, 1981
Published in English by David & Charles 1982
Revised English edition published by David & Charles 1994

A catalogue record for this book is available
from the British Library.

ISBN 0 7153 0203 5

Printed in Italy by LEGO SpA, Vicenza
for David & Charles
Brunel House   Newton Abbot   Devon

PREFACE

What exactly is meant by wild herbs? For the purposes of this book, a herb is defined as a plant which one gathers or grows with a specific aim: to cure, to feed, to enhance one's dishes or one's lifestyle, to dye wool, or for any other deliberate purpose. It can be regarded as a useful plant, provided that this convenient tag does not give the impression that all other plants are useless. It is all too easy to contrast 'good' herbs with 'bad' ones, and there are many plants which are useful among those regarded as 'bad'. The herbs in this book cover grasses and herbaceous plants, shrubs and trees. Their vernacular names are fascinating: they may be connected with a person, an animal or their specific property – herb Robert, catmint, wartwort.

A medicinal herb is considered as such in relation to the healing qualities attributed to it; its role is to provide a cure whatever the means by which it is used. If it is used pharmaceutically, it becomes officinal; if allopathy neglects it, it could still be homoeopathic; in the case of a medical treatment which recommends the use of plant essences, one talks of aromatherapy. Plants have always played a part in the art of healing, official or alternative, a part which varied according to the beliefs of the time. Proud of its chemosynthesis, the twentieth century has tended to overlook these herbs, but the natural methods of healing by vegetal means – herbal remedies – have brought them back with a vengeance. This resurgence contributed to the return to nature, which unfortunately could turn out to be just a fashion or a snare.

The tag 'wild herbs' obviously does not cover the plants widely cultivated and modified, finally even improved by such cultivation; it applies to those which are still in their natural state or which, long since acclimatized, can hardly be distinguished today from the native species. This definition excludes from this guide all cultivated herbs, particularly those whose connexion with wild species is remote or even unknown; this applies, notwithstanding their virtues, to the onion and the garlic, corn, parsley, olive tree and castor-oil plant, and many others. The same applies to herbs more recently introduced, or which have naturalized exceptionally quickly: nasturtiums, coriander, aniseed and tarragon cannot be numbered among the wild herbs of Western Europe.

But do all wild herbs appear in this book? Certainly not. We thought it better to leave out the rare and protected plants (cyclamen, pasqueflower, sundew, pheasant's-eye, Alpine mugwort) and to include only those common species capable of surviving the harvesting which threatens their existence. Indeed, in Great Britain the Conservation of

Wild Creatures and Wild Plants Act 1974 makes it an offence for any unauthorized person without reasonable excuse to uproot any wild plant (see page 205 for more details). Finally, from these common or relatively widespread species, we culled most of the poisonous plants – such as thorn-apple, or black nightshade – which have nothing to do with vernacular medicine. This was a difficult and somewhat arbitrary choice because, just like a rare plant which often exists only on a regional or local level, a toxic plant is difficult to define. It is all a matter of dosage and, in certain circumstances, even a simple infusion of camomile can be harmful.

Within the scope so far described, the assortment of wild herbs covered in this book is after all based on the authors' choice: a choice very carefully considered but still open to substitution or additions. Notwithstanding its shortcomings, we hope this guide will pave the way for a comprehensive work which will include all those herbs we regretfully had to leave out.

Last but not least, this guide is above all the work of two botanists. As such, it suggests the first steps towards a better knowledge of plants endowed with particular virtues – above all healing ones – while refraining from encroaching upon the medical domain. Our guide would like to complement, up to a certain point, those phytotherapeutic works whose botanical content is too often outmoded, incomplete and even useless; it aspires to being the launching pad into a marvellous world full of colour, perfume, taste and life.

HOW TO USE THIS GUIDE

The descriptive table is the main tool in the guide, conceived in such a way as to offer the essential information about any given herb. Such information is conveyed in graphic form through the use of pictograms, the detailed meaning of which is explained below as well as in the cover flaps.

This conception of a book based on the use of symbols[1] enables one to avoid long descriptions, while providing information in a consistent and uniform manner. It is not without fault in that it tends to over-simplify the data and cannot reproduce the slight variations and the diversity of real life, but this can be overcome firstly by turning to one of the Appendices at the end of this volume and secondly by referring to those works which are still based on the time-honoured system of written information (see Further Reading).

A. GENERAL NOTES

1. In order to find a herb, look among the pages marked in the margin by the colour corresponding to that of the flower of the plant. Choose from among the colour plates the one which most closely resembles the plant.
2. Each of the 144 photographs carries above it the number of the plate and the vernacular name. Choosing the latter has been difficult as many popular names are given to plants; we settled for the one which, to our knowledge, is the most widely used. Regional names frequently used, if that should be the case, are given in Appendix I (Botanical Notes).
3. Underneath the photograph the reader will find, on the left, the botanical name in latin of the species illustrated and, on the right, the family to which it belongs.

    The latin name is the only unequivocal reference of the species: according to the binomial nomenclature, it is composed of the name of the genus (the first one, eg *Rumex*, pl 1) and of the specific epithet (eg *alpinus*, pl 1). For the sake of consistency, we have followed the nomenclature given by *Flora Europaea*[2] even when differing from current usage: in these cases, the most common synonym is given in

---

[1] Several of these pictograms are based on the system suggested by Stefenelli, *Fiori della Montagna*, Priuli & Verlucca, 1977.

[2] Tutin, T. G., *et al*; Cambridge University Press. Vol 1 1964; vol 2 1968; vol 3 1972; vol 4 1976; vol 5 1980.

the botanical note relating to the particular species (Appendix I) and in the index. The latin name is always followed by the name (often shortened) of the botanist who first described the species in question (eg L. as abbreviation of Linnaeus, after *Rumex alpinus*, pl 1).

4. Opposite the plate number and the vernacular name, four pictograms show, by being coloured yellow, first of all whether the plant is a medicinal one, then whether a plant accepted in homoeopathy, whether an aromatic plant, and finally whether a culinary plant. If the symbol is coloured red instead of yellow, one should be very careful as the species could be toxic, at least in parts.

5. The three groups of pictograms on the lower half of the page allow the reader firstly to verify whether, on the basis of the botanical peculiarities expressed by the symbols, the choice of plate is the right one; secondly, to gather the ecological characteristics exemplified by the group of pictograms which surround the map (habitat, geographical distribution, phenology, etc); and lastly to find out which organ of the plant can be picked and when.

   The distribution of the species throughout Europe is shown in the map, which was based on data taken from Meusel[3], Walter[4], and Hulten[5]; when the species did not appear in any of these works, the approximate distribution was traced on the basis of information found in *Flora Europaea*.

6. The three Appendices appearing after the colour plates are designed first of all to complement the 'identity card' of the species (possible confusion with similar species not illustrated, further botanical characteristics, synonyms, etc, in Appendix I), and secondly to supplement the information summarized at the bottom of the plate pages, particularly in the therapeutic field (Appendix II) and culinary uses (Appendix III).

[3] Meusel, H., Jäger, E. and Weinert, E., *Vergleichende Chorologie der Zentraleuropaeischen Flora*, Verlag G. Fisher, Iena 1965, Vol 1 (text) and 2 (maps).

[4] Walter, H., *Einführung in die Phytologie. III. Grundlagen der Pflanzenverbreitung. II. Teil arealkunde.,* Verlag E. Ulmer, Stuttgart 1954.

[5] Hulten, E., *The Circumpolar Plants*, Almqvist & Wiksell, Stockholm. Vol 1 1964, vol 2 1971.

B. THE MEANING OF THE SYMBOLS

I. TABLE OF BOTANICAL SYMBOLS

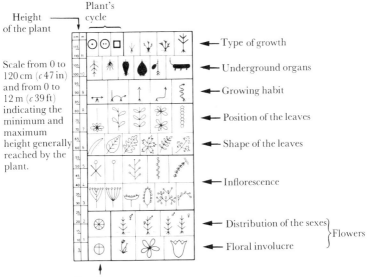

Plant's cycle

Annual plant: a plant which only lasts one season.

Biennial plant: a plant which survives for two consecutive seasons. In the first year it only develops its stems and leaves; in the second, flowers and fruits appear, and the cycle is completed.

Perennial plant: a plant which survives for longer than two years without actually becoming entirely woody.

Type of growth and height of the plant

Herbaceous: a plant having the appearance and consistency of grass.

Under-shrub: a plant the stem of which is woody at the base and herbaceous in the upper parts.

Shrub or bush: a woody plant, with branches almost from ground level, reaching a height from 1 to 5 m (c 3–16 ft).

7

Tree: a much larger woody plant with a cylindrical trunk and woody ramifications forming the framework of the upper part.

Whatever the type of growth, the average minimum and maximum height is indicated in the scale to the left of the table of symbols.

Underground organs

Tap-root: main root, elongated, from which lateral roots radiate (called secondary roots) and in turn ramificate. It is attached to the collar of the plant right opposite the stem.

Fasciculate roots: a system of several thin roots of equal importance and all descending from the collar.

Fleshy root: a tap-root in the shape of an upside-down cone, or sometimes more or less spherical.

Bulb: an underground stem, extremely short and protected by leaf-like layers more or less fleshy; fasciculate roots emanate from the lower part of the bulb.

Tuber: a swollen and fleshy underground stem, provided with buds and filled with reserve substances.

Rhizome: underground stem, more or less horizontal and knotty. It differs from a root in being provided with buds from which grow above-ground stems. The real roots appear underneath the knots.

Growing habit

Spreading: a plant with ramifications of various length spreading out on the soil.

Stoloniferous: a plant with branches spread on the soil and forming, at more or less regular intervals, groups of random roots from the middle of which a young plant grows and can eventually become self-supporting.

Erect: bushy or arborescent herbaceous plant with stem(s) growing straight up from the base.

Rambling: a plant with stem(s) spreading on the soil near the base and becoming erect in their upper parts.

Climbing: a plant with a generally slender stem clinging to other plants or to various supports by means of tendrils or adhering discs; or a plant the stem of which grows by twining itself around the support.

Position of leaves on the stem

Rosette: leaves arranged at the base of the plant around a short axis which grows into a stem or a flower stalk.

Alternate: leaves growing on the stem or branch at different intervals and different levels.

Opposite: leaves growing in pairs on the same level but opposed to each other.

Whorled: more than two leaves growing at the same level of the stem or branch.

Imbricated: small leaves growing partially on top of one another like roof tiles.

Shape of leaves

Single narrow leaves; needle-shaped, linear, lanceolate, spatulate.

Single wide leaves, profile unbroken or slightly dented; oval, obovate, elliptical, round, cordiform, sagittate.

Single leaves with more or less incised or lobed edges; lobed, laciniate, pinnatifid.

Single leaves indented almost to the centre in the shape of a fan; palmate leaves.

Composite leaves showing variously shaped folioles which can in turn be dented and attached to the same axis: trifoliolated, pinnate, bipinnate, palmate.

Inflorescence
(distribution of the flowers on the plant)

Plant without flowers: lichens, seaweeds, mosses, ferns – the sexual organs of which are not apparent.

Single flower: a plant with either one single flower or several isolated ones.

Raceme or cluster: inflorescence formed by a length of stem supporting pedicillate flowers. The symbol covers both the single and the composite racemes (certain panicles).

Spike: a usually straight inflorescence carrying sessile flowers along a central axis and at different levels. The symbol also covers those inflorescences formed by composite spikes.

Amentum: a generally drooping inflorescence formed by small unisexual and sessile flowers, closely set on the stem. The same pictogram is used for the cones of the Gymnosperms.

Corymb: inflorescence formed by flowers having pedicils of uneven length which stem from different levels of the main axis but reach more or less the same height. Both single and composite corymbs are included.

Umbel: inflorescence formed by flowers the pedicils of which leave the main axis from the same point and attain a more or less even height. Both single and composite umbels are included.

Flat capitulum: the inflorescence is centred on a flat or convex receptacle; the flowers are sessile or have short pedicils, all of them are either ligulate or tubulate, sometimes arranged to look like a single flower.

Oblong capitulum: a globular, oblong or elongated inflorescence, with flowers all of the same kind, either sessiles or with brief pedicils, closely set along the axis.

Cyme: an inflorescence with primary ramifications which grow beyond the main axis (ending in a flower) and are eventually overtaken by secondary ramifications. The symbol shows a cyme with ramifications opposed in pairs but applies also to composite inflorescences (ie panicles formed by a group of cymes).

Curved cyme: a cyme in which the ramifications grow successively on one side only of the main axis, giving the structure a curved appearance.

Distribution of the sexes

Monoecious plant with hermaphrodite flowers: a plant with bisexual flowers: both the male organs (stamens) and the female ones (pistils) are part of the same flower.

Monoecious plant with unisexual flowers: the flowers are either male (♂) or female (♀), both on the same plant.

Dioecious plant: a plant having flowers of one sex only, either only males or only females.

Floral symmetry

Flower with radial symmetry (several symmetrical planes).

Flowers with bilateral symmetry (a single symmetrical plane).

Floral involucres

Bare flowers: flowers having no involucre.

Flowers with independent petals (the parts of the chalice, where this exists, can be independent or sometimes welded).

Flowers with petals welded at least at the base, thus forming a cup more or less bell-shaped and more or less lobed.

II. DISTRIBUTION, HABITAT AND PHENOLOGY

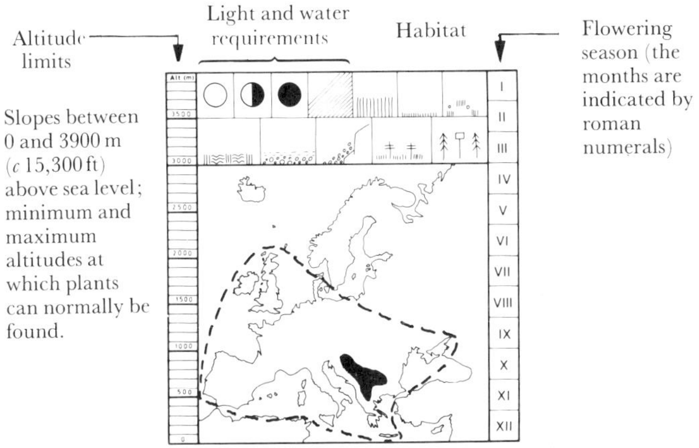
Light and water requirements
Habitat
Altitude limits
Flowering season (the months are indicated by roman numerals)
Slopes between 0 and 3900 m (c 15,300 ft) above sea level; minimum and maximum altitudes at which plants can normally be found.
Alt (m)
3500
3000
2500
2000
1500
1000
500
0
I
II
III
IV
V
VI
VII
VIII
IX
X
XI
XII

Distribution map
(eg: feverfew, pl 87)

■ : area where the species is indigenous
- - - : area where the species has become naturalized

Light requirements

In full sun.

In half-shaded position.

In the shade.

Humidity requirements

Marshy soil, humid or cool. If this symbol is not coloured, the plant is a xerophile, or has no particular requirements as to the humidity of the soil.

Habitat

Wild grassland.

Pastures, meadows.

Wasteland, verges, fallow soil, hedgerows.

Peatbogs and fens.

Sandbanks, river banks, marshes.

Rocky banks, cliffs, stony soils, dry walls.

Heaths and moors.

Forests and copses.

III. PLANT PARTS TO BE GATHERED AND TIME OF GATHERING

Parts to be gathered

Most favourable time of gathering (the months are indicated by roman numerals).

If two different plant organs are used and if they are not picked at the same time, the most favourable seasons for the picking are indicated by the colours used for the organs in question. For instance, common sorrel (pl 2) should have its leaves picked in the spring and summer, while the rhizome is collected in the autumn.

Plant parts to be gathered

 The whole plant; roots, stem, leaves and flowers.

 Leaves.

 Stems with their leaves.

 Stems.

 Buds.

 Bark.

 Roots.

 Resin, latex.

 Bulb.

 Rhizome.

 Flowers (in bud or picked just as they begin to open).

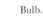 Fruits.

Seeds.

Thallus (algae, lichens).

INTRODUCTION TO THE USE OF HERBS

It is self-evident that medicinal plants are used for therapeutic purposes. On the other hand, aromatic herbs have less well-defined roles, which may be medicinal or medicinal and culinary. Culinary herbs often have medicinal properties and are aromatic and flavoursome, almost by definition. Most plants included in this field guide have a number of properties, even if they are best known for one in particular.

Whether medicinal, aromatic or culinary, all these herbs with multiple purposes are so closely linked that it is difficult to tell where the speciality of one begins and that of another ends. One only has to consult a dictionary for evidence that it is difficult to distinguish an aromatic herb from a condiment. A condiment (or seasoning) is any substance with a strong taste used to add flavour to foodstuffs; apart from salt, all condiments have a plant origin, just like all spices and aromatics. The latter, as implied by their name, are mainly used to impart a fragrance, but their sweetness does not prevent them from conferring a sharp flavour to the dishes they are used to season.

However one distinguishes between condiments and aromatic herbs the terms are irrelevant to the ways in which they are exploited both by the chef and the physician. A physician is first of all a therapist, and uses his or her knowledge to alleviate, cure or prevent an illness. If sometimes herbs are used for this purpose, the physician becomes the prescriber of a mild medicine, thus joining in the efforts of the dietician or of the real cook, who tries not only to render their dishes more agreeable but to prepare them with the health of his guests in mind.

1. ACTIVE AGENTS AND DRUGS

A herb's qualities are a reflection of the presence of substances which have been produced by plant metabolism. It is these substances which are the active agents. The combined effect of these has been known in some cases for a very long time indeed, even though it may not have been possible to find out how they worked within our bodies. It is only recently that the active substances have been isolated chemically and their therapeutic effects tested, then compared with that of the substances extracted from other herbs with a similar overall effect, and finally synthesized.

A herbalist distinguishes between a plant preparation – ie the vegetal matter in its entirety, whether fresh or dried, which is used directly or indirectly in the preparation of a remedy – and the active agents, either extracted from the plant or, if the specific agent is known, synthesized.

The mainstream of modern medicine ignores and neglects natural plants and considers as important only the pure active agents. And yet in some cases the active agents, although easier to prescribe in the right quantity and more effective in the case of acute afflictions, can actually produce too strong a reaction. The plant from which it originates, however, would not. The effect of a plant preparation is slower over a period of time but sometimes more complete: it progressively releases substances which are highly absorbable by the organism and acts in a considerably milder way.

The complex 'arsenal' of active agents which can be present in a plant preparation creates problems which are difficult to assess in the light of our present knowledge. One is aware of favourable results having been achieved by the synergy of two active principles both present in the same plant; the synergic action produces results which are definitely superior to those which might have been achieved by each of the two elements acting separately. But is our present, insufficient understanding reason enough to refute the results achieved so far, however modest they might be?

2. NATURAL CHARACTERISTICS OF THE ACTIVE PRINCIPLES

The effectiveness of the centuries-old use of herbs can only be verified by analysing the active principles extracted from them and the way in which they act. The results, albeit provisional, of such research allows us to come up with answers, however sketchy, to the various questions. Which are the active substances or, to put it another way, which among the hundreds of chemicals we know today, are the large 'families' of active agents? What is their role in the vegetal world? How do they act?

Thanks to photosynthesis, all green plants produce sugars – or, to be more exact, glucides – which are adapted and eventually transformed into more complex molecules such as fats (or lipids). But apart from these basic metabolic derivatives, there are many other substances without any clear role. They are often regarded as waste products although they undoubtedly have roles as yet unknown within the plants themselves. Whatever their origins they are very useful to mankind. The accepted active agents from among the products secreted – or sometimes excreted – by plant cells can be roughly grouped as follows.

A. The heterosides

These active agents are exceptionally varied and by far the most commonly represented together with the alkaloids (see C).

Roughly speaking, they consist of sugars combined with chemical substances of a totally different nature: hence the first half of their name, *hetero* meaning *other*. The glucidic half of these compounds allows them to be soluble and absorbable by the organism.

Each heteroside family is characterized by the nature of the non-sugary part of the molecule; this appears to have particular properties and can act selectively upon one or more organs of the human body. Once isolated, the substance linked to the sugar in the plant can prove to be toxic: it is the association with the sugar which, provisionally and up to a point, neutralizes it.

The heteroside chemistry is obviously complex and far from clear. The examples below will allow us to understand, however vaguely, the behaviour of the active principles.

(1) THE PHENOLIC HETEROSIDES

Grouped within this denomination are a great number of heterosides in which sugars are coupled with simple or more or less complex phenols, even polyphenols.

a. *Simple phenolic compounds*

Grouped here are the simplest heterosides; these were the first to be discovered, particularly salicin which is the basis of salicylic compounds encountered not only in the willow but also in the meadowsweet (pl 63), sometimes called 'vegetal aspirain'; its febrifuge effects are well-known.

b. *Tannins*

The phenolic group here becomes more complex. Once liberated, it forms new compositions with proteins (which precipitate), alkaloids (which precipitate and are neutralized) and the cellulose of the plant's linings (particularly in the bark and woody parts rendered undecomposable by tannin).

The organs with a high level of tannin have a high degree of astringency (alder bark, pl 20; tormentil rhizomes, pl 35; bramble leaves, pl 79; bistort root, pl 111): their action on the mucous membranes, or on wounds and burns, produces a superficial coagulation, which in turn generates a protective layer that speeds up the healing process. This waterproofing produced by contact with tannins explains their properties as antidiarrhoeics.

c. *Anthracenoids*

A name derived from a combination of sugars and anthracene (substance derived from anthracite and the basic ingredient of many colourants). Their sugar content is associated with a phenolic nucleus which is eventually 'digested' by bile and transformed into a more or less potent laxative according to the species of plant. These laxatives only act upon the large intestine (monk's rhubarb, pl 1; common sorrel, pl 2; common buckthorn, pl 24; alder buckthorn, pl 65).

d. *Polyphenolic heterosides*

These heterosides, when combined with glucides, produce natural polyphenols, some of which are colourless while others are yellow (flavonoids) and have long since been known for their properties as colourants. They affect blood circulation and are instrumental in the correction of blood pressure. This is particularly so in the case of the hawthorn (pl 76).

The plant extracts containing these heterosides prove themselves useful in the treatment of blood vessels by improving their strength, thus avoiding small haemorrhages (see rue, pl 32). Many are also used as antispasmodics (see silverweed, pl 36).

(2) SAPONISIDES

This complex group of heterosides includes, among others, those substances characterized by a non-glucidic constituent soluble in water and apt to make it foam. They have a varied effect on the human body. Their irritant properties are used to aid expectoration (cowslip, pl 47; goldenrod, pl 51; daisy, pl 85; soapwort, pl 100).

These substances also possess diuretic properties (downy birch, pl 19; dog's mercury, pl 23).

B. Mucilages

Mucilages are also complex glucidic compounds quite widespread in the plant world. They contribute to the nutritional reserves and to water economy. Plant extracts rich in mucilagenous substances (ribwort plantain, pl 5; colt's-foot, pl 52; marsh mallow, pl 102; borage, pl 137) provide us with viscous elements which cover the mucous membranes and soothe irritations. They can also be used as laxatives owing to the swelling they cause in the intestines.

C. Alkaloids

This group of nitrogenized substances is the basis for numerous allopathic treatments. It includes some powerful poisons which act on the central nervous system (hemlock's cicutoxin, poppy's morphine). Most of the plants containing them are also dangerous, and consequently their application must be exclusively external (eg the latex of the wartwort which contains chelidomine).

D. The bitter principles

This group of substances does not belong to a chemical family; all they have in common is a bitter taste. When taken internally, their bitterness stimulates the glands of the digestive duct causing them to secrete juices and enhance the appetite. As long as they are administered in the right dosage, extracts rich in bitter substances are therefore essentially used as aperitives, digestives and generally speaking stomachics (wormwood, pl 27; blessed thistle, pl 56; common centaury, pl 112; chicory, pl 140). Some of these plants are more effective as cholagogues to control the secretion of bile and choleretics to treat bilious cholera (dandelion, pl 55; large yellow gentian, pl 61).

E. The aromatic oils

The active agents belonging to this category are many, and most of them are aromatic and volatile; they are terpenic compounds. Their smell, however, can only be released by drying or bruising the plant organ in question. Some botanical families – such as the *Umbelliferae*, the *Labiatae* and the *Compositae* – are particularly rich in essences, and to them belong many aromatic and culinary herbs (wormwood, pl 27; winter savory, pl 91; wild angelica, pl 93; sage, pl 143).

Their action can be either as a stimulant of the central nervous system (wormwood, pl 27) or as a sedative (valerian, pl 99).

As in the case of the bitters, some of these essences are stomachic and digestive (eg those of wild thyme, pl 109 and hyssop, pl 144); others are used as intestinal disinfectants (eg fennel, pl 30); others are expectorants, as they are expelled by the lungs (white horehound, pl 74; garden thyme, pl 98). Many are antiparasitic, antiseptic or vermifuge (cotton lavender, pl 54; feverfew, pl 87). Finally, other aromatic oils, particularly those found in the *Cruciferae*, have external applications; they can be used to treat rheumatism as they stimulate the circulation (powdered charlock, pl 48).

The essences sometimes oxidize within the plant and form resins.

F. Mineral elements

Mineral substances have a separate place in this list as their therapeutic action is only slight as long as they are part of a well-balanced diet (iron, calcium, potash, iodine).

Some herbs are rich in minerals and their effect is therefore more marked. Silica, an important element where skin and nails are concerned, is found in specially large quantities in the horsetail (pl 12) and knotgrass (pl 73).

G. Vitamins

Vitamins are indispensable to life and yet the metabolism of all animals, including man, is unable to synthesize them; they have to be extracted from fresh vegetables. Among the vitamin-rich plants described in this guide are carrots (pl 71) which contain vitamin A, sea buckthorn (pl 17) and the dog-rose (pl 92) for their high levels of vitamin C (antiscorbutic), and the watercress (pl 90), well endowed with vitamin E, necessary for the functioning of the muscles.

3. THE PLANT ORGANS MOST COMMONLY USED

Active agents are not equally distributed within a plant. Each of the organs has its own structural and functional properties; it is not surprising, therefore, that the botanical remedies, aromatics and seasonings should be composed of only one organ or even by parts of organs particularly rich in active agents. By the same token, the organs which are sought after for their properties differ between one botanical species and another.

With certain herbs, the preparation is the whole plant or, more often, those organs appearing above the ground; to the former group belongs St John's wort (pl 49), to the latter the common yarrow (pl 94).

Of all the plant organs, leaves and roots occupy a special place for their high level of active substances. The leaf is above all where the synthesis takes place: here one finds the numerous alkaloids (white bryony, pl 67), heterosides (ramsons, pl 82) and aromatic essences (bay, pl 64). The substances dissolved in the soil are absorbed through the roots: sugars, aromatic oils (lesser burdock, pl 121), vitamins (wild carrot, pl 71), glucose (white bryony, pl 67) and many other compounds are to be found there.

The stem is mainly a 'transit' organ, rather than contributing to the synthesizing or stocking-up of the trace elements. It is, nevertheless, often gathered with the leaves (common sorrel, pl 2), particularly when the young shoots are picked and used fresh (watercress, pl 90). Even old and woody stems can contain active agents, particularly in the bark (downy birch, pl 19; alder, pl 20) or in the young wood (lime sap-wood, pl 33). And just like the roots, the underground stems, usually modified, are often rich in various substances: tubercles have plenty of glucides, rhizomes of masterwort (pl 69) supply aromatic oils and those of the soapwort (pl 100) the saponisides; and the bulbs of garlic are full of oils with antibiotic properties. Finally, the tips of the branches of shrubs and trees can also contain complex compounds much in demand (aromatic oils in the shoots of the Scots pine, pl 15).

The reproductive organs, whether asexual or sexual, also provide drugs or important aromatics in all the various stages of their development (buds, open flowers, fruits and seeds), as do the parts themselves of such organs (style and stigmas of saffron, floral pedicils of the cherry flower). One gathers either the individual organs, such as the flower buds (cloves), the flowers just before they open (common mallow, pl 114), the ripe fruits (diachaeniums of fennel, pl 30; berries of sea buckthorn, pl 17) or the seeds (charlock, pl 48); or a group of organs, such as the capitulums of the *Compositae* (mountain tobacco, pl 43; daisy, pl 85); the floral spikes composed of the stems of the inflorescence, the bracts and the flowers and, in some cases, of the nearby stems with the leaves (motherwort, pl 104; ling, pl 117; rosemary, pl 130), and even the whole of the flowering plant (fumitory, pl 113; wild teasel, pl 129).

Finally, the product excreted by the plant is sometimes gathered instead of any particular organ; such is the case of certain resins and of the latex (greater celandine, pl 40).

It is therefore obvious that it is extremely important to have some elementary knowledge of a plant's structure before attempting to gather it. It is not only a question of recognizing the particular botanical species but also of knowing which organs produce the active substances.

4. SHOULD HERBS BE GATHERED OR CULTIVATED?

One of the aims of this guide is to encourage the knowledge of herbs. In order to do this, two complementary courses can be followed: random gathering during specially organized walks or setting up a small herb garden for personal or family use. In Great Britain, the restrictions of the Conservation of Wild Creatures and Wild Plants Act 1974 on picking wild flowers and plants must be observed (see page 205).

Both these ways of getting to know plants have always existed side by side; even when, in the countryside, the gathering of medicinal plants was part of the domestic work, the herbs most difficult to find or imported in the earliest times were often cultivated in the gardens surrounding the houses. It followed naturally that the richest collections should be built by those who possessed the key to knowledge and barter: the rich herb gardens of abbeys and monasteries have sometimes survived to the present day even if by now they are to most people only a curiosity.

However, ancient practices are making a come-back and new herb gardens flourish: faculties which had expressly abandoned them as old-fashioned now tolerate them, but without giving them the recognition and support they deserve and without adding the subjects related to them to the curriculum of medical or pharmaceutical students. For example, a garden of medicinal herbs was planted in the grounds of the Faculty of Medicine, Catholic University of Louvain near Brussels in Belgium.

a. The first rule to be observed by anyone deciding to look out for useful herbs – culinary or medicinal – is to respect our common inheritance: the wild herbs.

One should never pick too many.

One should pick only as many as are strictly necessary to cover one's needs until the new season; many medicinal and aromatic remedies lose their properties in time and it is an excellent rule to renew them annually.

One should only pick those species which will be effectively used, according to one's taste and the demands of one's health.

One should also be careful to pick in such a way as not to compromise the multiplication and propagation of a species, particularly when this is a rare one – even if only locally.

Finally, one should pick them with care, so as not to damage the environment.

b. With these rules in mind, the gathering should be carried out in the right season, following the annual botanical rhythm: picking herbs is only worth while at the exact moment when the particular organs possess the greatest quantity of active principles. It is therefore necessary to compile a picking calendar: one should be able to visit the same place over and over again, according to whether one gathers the bark in winter, the buds in spring, the leaves at the beginning of summer, the flowers in mid-summer or the roots in the autumn.

In the case of each of the species mentioned in this guide, the best time of the year in which to gather the useful organ is indicated by the symbols. Generally speaking, medicinal herbs should be gathered in the morning, when the dew has dried and the weather is fine, or better still after a brief period of dry weather. The safe keeping of the products depends on this.

c. Once the gathering calendar is in working order, one should choose the itineraries between the areas of potential picking. Here the rules are very simple. All places can be good in theory, but one should choose remote areas, sheltered from the effects of modern civilization: avoid the verges of busy roads, contaminated by dust and exhaust fumes; avoid the embankments which have been systematically sprayed with insecticides; avoid also the edges of large fields notwithstanding the richness of their occasional flora, as the colour of the poppies, camomile and fumitories, particularly where beet is cultivated, can hide high concentrations of pesticides.

Secluded country footpaths, with their diversified habitats, suit admirably, as well as the open spaces of moors and heaths for such plants as broom and ling.

d. Take care in particular to pick the healthiest herbs, without traces of insects or snails.

Carefully pick the useful parts by cutting them, without tearing the branches or lacerating the leaves. This will help in conserving them.

Take extra care to eliminate all parts irrelevant to the crop; the roots will need to be rinsed in water to free them from unwanted particles.

Sort out and separate immediately the various herbs and mark them carefully and individually.

Take your crop home in linen bags or baskets, keeping it ventilated; avoid hermetically closed containers where the herbs can deteriorate.

e. Cultivating herbs, together with gathering them, may well be the answer to domestic needs. The demands of pharmaceutical industries can only be satisfied by intensive cultivation.

Garden herbs are not necessarily less potent than wild ones. In order to obtain high levels of active principles, one should study the needs of each species, in other words their ecology. Each part of the environment can affect them, above all the soil (structure, texture, drainage, richness in nutrients . . .) and the exposure to light; the latter is affected by topographical as well as climatic conditions (and therefore related to altitude). To each herb its climate.

5. PREPARATION, DRYING AND STORAGE OF HERBS

As soon as you get your crop home, take steps to dry up the plant parts you want to preserve. This is done to prevent the onset of fermentation and to maintain at their best the properties of the plant.

a. The best way to dry the plant depends on its nature: either in the shade or in the sun, in the open or in a drying-room, in bunches or on racks . . . Only the herbs containing aromatic oils need to be dried in the shade; the others benefit from being exposed to the sun, but for no longer than is necessary for the drying process.

Plants containing aromatic oils need a temperature ranging between 20 and 40°C (58 to 104°F); if this is not possible in the open, one should briefly place them in the oven. In all other cases, the temperature can range from 15 to 70°C (60 to 140°F).

The last rule to be followed concerns the ventilation of the plant organs being dried. Bunches should be suspended in a well ventilated room, other parts should be spread in thin layers on cloths and regularly turned.

The fleshy organs (roots and rhizomes) should first be cut into small pieces – except for species containing aromatic oils.

The time required by the drying process obviously varies with the temperature, the ventilation, the relative humidity of the air and the water content of the organs themselves; it should not take longer than two or three days for flowers, and a maximum of eight days for tight bunches.

b. The preservation of the herbs requires hermetically closed containers (glass or china jars are better than metal or plastic containers). The herbs should then be kept away from direct light in a dry store-room.

Do not forget to label each container carefully, writing down the date when the plant was picked.

THE FIELD GUIDE

THE FIELD GUIDE

The photographs in the book are the work of the authors except plates 17 and 84 which are by Gilbert Garot, and 106 and 115 by Paul Sterry, Nature Photographers Ltd.

ABBREVIATIONS:

Seas: used for seasoning
Ext: to be used externally
Int: to be used internally
Syn: synonym
Dye: used in the dye industry
Perf: used in the perfume industry

Rumex alpinus L.   Polygonaceae

Properties: *Int:* laxative (no dangerous secondary effects).

Rumex acetosa L.   Polygonaceae

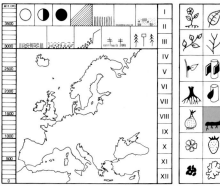

Properties: *Int:* diuretic (rhizome); antiscorbutic due to its high content of vit C (aerial parts, above all the leaves).

Polygonum hydropiper L.   Polygonaceae

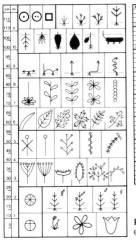

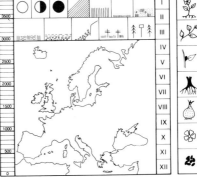

Properties: *Int:* astringent, haemostatic, antihaemorroidal, emmenagogue (particularly the fresh plant).

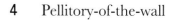

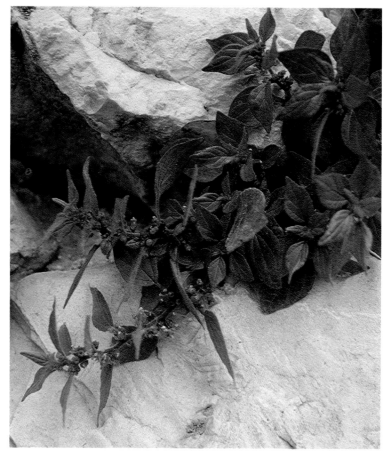

Parietaria diffusa Mert. and Koch   Urticaceae

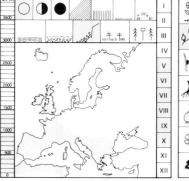

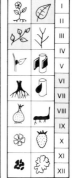

Properties: *Int:* diuretic, depurative (particularly the leaves). *Ext:* vulnerary (treatment of burns).

Plantago lanceolata L.   Plantaginaceae

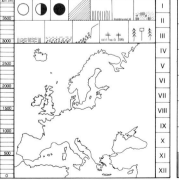

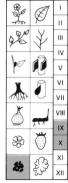

Properties: *Int:* astringent, haemostatic, antidiarrhoeic; controls intestinal movements thanks to the mucilages which coat the seeds; emollient and expectorant (respiratory ducts). *Ext:* cicatrizing, soothing, anti-inflammatory (sores, burns, insect bites).

Artemisia vulgaris L.   Compositae

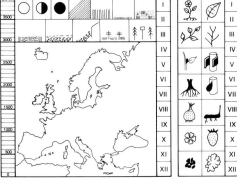

Properties: *Int:* tonic, digestive, cholagogue, antispasmodic; emmenagogue (to be taken with care). *Seas:* flowers and leaves. The pollen is the cause of several allergies (hay fever).

Anthoxanthum odoratum L.   Graminaceae

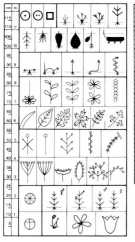

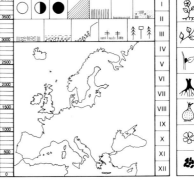

Properties: *Ext:* antirheumatic; sedative.

Urtica dioica L.   Urticaceae

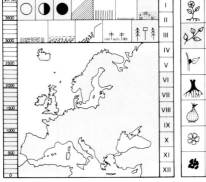

Properties: *Int:* anti-anaemic (rich in vit C); diuretic (uricolytic) and depurative; hypoglycemic; stomachic; haemostatic; antidiarrhoeic. *Ext:* haemostatic (nose-bleeds).

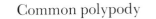

Polypodium vulgare L.   Polypodiaceae

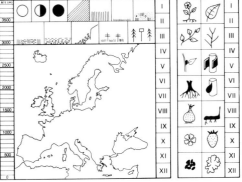

Properties: *Int:* vermifuge; expectorant and bechic; cholagogue and laxative. The rhizome contains sugary mucilages and can be used mashed, although somewhat bitter.

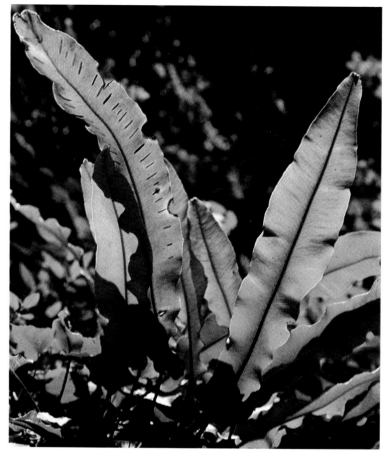

Phyllitis scolopendrium (L.) Newman   Aspleniaceae

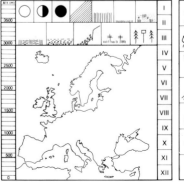

Properties: *Int:* astringent and antidiarrhoeic; bechic; cholagogue.

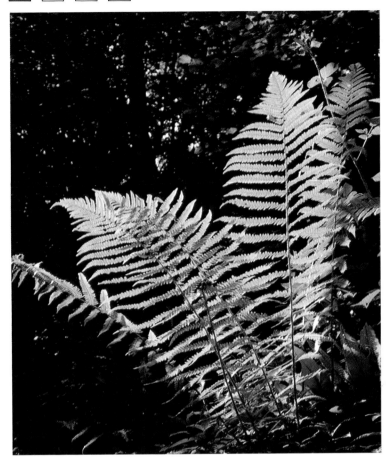

Dryopteris filix-mas (L.) Schott Aspidiaceae

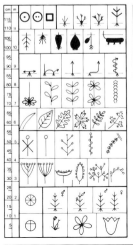

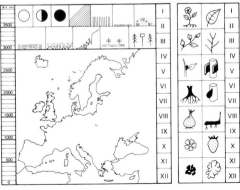

Properties: *Int:* powerful vermifuge (particularly tapeworm); the drug is toxic and must be used with great care. *Ext:* cicatrizing.

Equisetum arvense L.

Equisetaceae

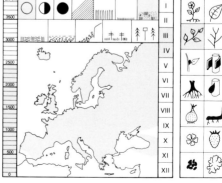

Properties: *Int:* rich in minerals; diuretic; haemostatic (uterine haemorrhages). *Ext:* haemostatic (nose-bleeds).

Juniperus oxycedrus L.   Cupressaceae

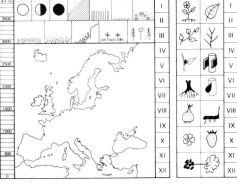

Properties: *Ext:* antiparasitic (veterinary use); effective cure of skin ailments (eczemas, psoriasis).

Juniperus communis L.   Cupressaceae

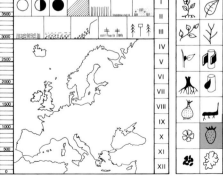

Properties: *Int:* diuretic (uxicolytic) depurative and antiseptic (branches and berries); tonic and stomachic, carminative (berries). *Ext:* rubefacient, antirheumatic. *Seas:* berries are used in the preparation of several liqueurs.

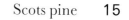

Pinus sylvestris L.   Pinaceae

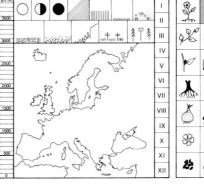

Properties: *Int:* balsamic, bechic, light diuretic (buds). *Ext:* vulnerary (buds); antirheumatic (needles).

Elymus repens (L.) Gould   Graminaceae

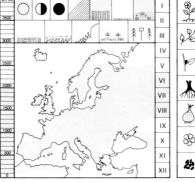

Properties: *Int:* diuretic, depurative, anti-inflammatory of the urinary ducts; febrifuge.

Hippophae rhamnoides L.   Eleagnaceae

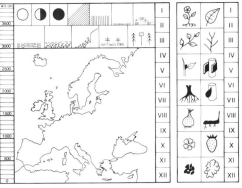

Properties: *Int:* biocatalyst, tonic (leaves, and above all fruits, are extremely rich in vit A and C and carotene); laxative, diuretic, anti-inflammatory. *Seas:* dried fruits (either whole or powdered), or even fresh, as substitutes for lemons.

Salicornia europaea L.   Chenopodiaceae

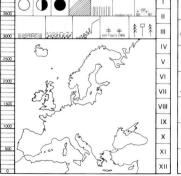

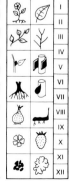

Properties: *Int:* diuretic and depurative; rich in minerals (such as potassium, sodium, iodine); antiscorbutic (vit C). *Seas.:* the herb makes a pleasant seasoning when pickled in vinegar.

Betula pubescens Ehrh.   Betulaceae

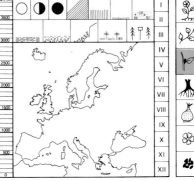

Properties: *Int*: diuretic, chlorurolytic, nephritic, disinfectant of the urinary ducts, sudorific (leaves); choleretic (buds); febrifuge (bark). *Ext*: disinfectant of the skin (bark). The tar extracted from the distilled bark is used in the preparation of Russian leather. *Dye*: a great variety of shades according to the mordancy.

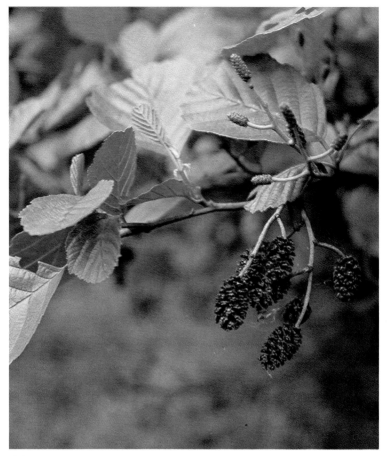

Alnus glutinosa (L.) Gaertner   Betulaceae

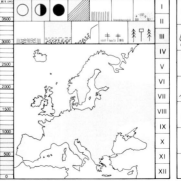

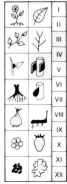

Properties: *Int:* tonic and febrifuge, its action is somewhat similar to that of Peruvian bark; antilacteous. *Dye:* bright yellow or grey tones, according to the parts being used.

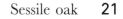

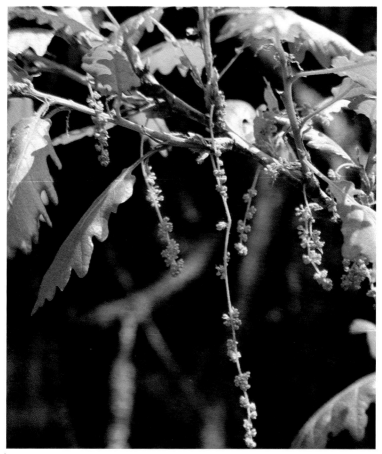

Quercus petraea (Matt.) Lieblein   Fagaceae

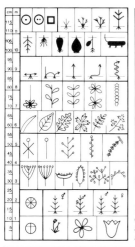

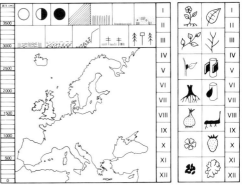

Properties: *Int:* strong astringent due to its high tannin content, antiseptic, antidiarrhoeic; tonic. Roasted acorns can advantageously replace coffee. *Dye:* brown or beige tones according to the preparation.

Fraxinus excelsior L.   Oleaceae

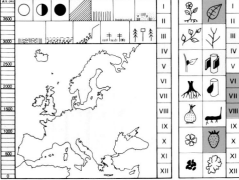

Properties: *Int:* febrifuge (European equivalent of the Peruvian bark), bitter and astringent (young bark, seeds); diuretic, uricolytic, light laxative, antirheumatic (young leaves). *Dye:* grey-green tones.

Mercurialis perennis L.   Euphorbiaceae

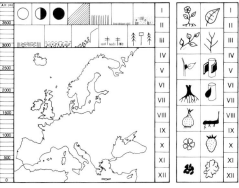

Properties: *Int:* diuretic, laxative (particularly the fresh plant). *Dye:* wool becomes pale yellow if dye is fixed with alum.

Rhamnus catharticus L.   Rhamnaceae

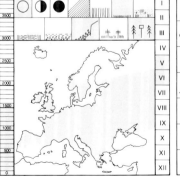

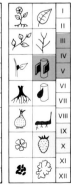

Properties: *Int:* strong laxative which can cause vomiting and bleeding (to be used only on medical prescription).

Humulus lupulus L.

Cannabaceae

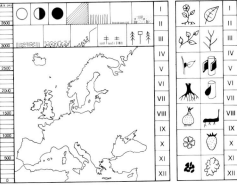

Properties: *Int:* bitter tonic, stomachic, aperitive; narcotic, sedative and anaphrodisiac; bacteriostatic; oestrogenic action.

Crithmun maritimum L.   Umbelliferae

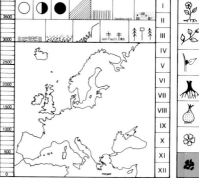

Properties: *Int:* aperitive, tonic, diuretic; vermifuge (fresh juice or seeds). *Seas:* leaves can be used to prepare an aromatic vinegar as well as a seasoning when pickled in vinegar.

Artemisia absinthium L.   Compositae

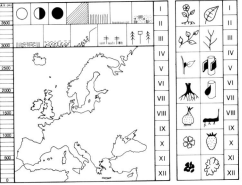

Properties: *Int:* bitter tonic, digestive, anti-nausea; febrifuge; emmenagogue; vermifuge. *Ext:* antiseptic. Insecticide (concentrated distillation). Used as an aromatic (absinth wine) in the production of liqueurs (vermouth), its essence is toxic (epileptic complaints).

Aristolochia clematitis L.   Aristolochiaceae

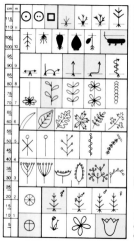

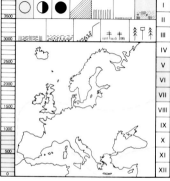

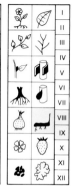

Properties: *Int:* dangerous emmenagogue as in strong doses can cause abortions; sedative of the nervous system; drastic. *Ext:* vulnerary, cicatrizing.

Galium verum L.   Rubiaceae

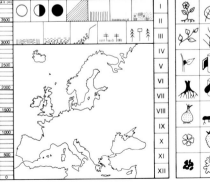

Properties: *Int:* diuretic; antispasmodic and sedative (slight nervous afflictions, migraines, palpitations). *Ext:* mild astringent used against ulcers and dermatitis.

Foeniculum vulgare Miller

Umbelliferae

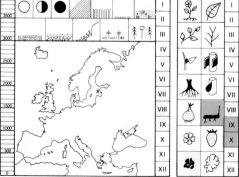

Properties: *Int:* diuretic, aperitive, digestive (fruit and rhizome); carminative, galactagogue, antispasmodic (fruit). *Seas:* both leaves and fruits can be used for seasoning; the fruits contain an essence used in the preparation of aromatic beverages (aniseed).

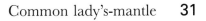

Alchemilla xanthochlora Rothm.   Rosaceae

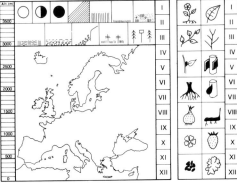

Properties: *Int:* tonic, astringent, depurative and diuretic; emmenagogue; antispasmodic (stomach). *Ext:* vulnerary, anti-pruriginous.

Ruta graveolens L.   Rutaceae

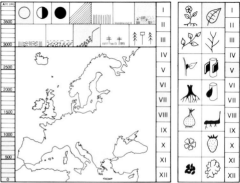

Properties: *Int:* abortive, emmenagogue; antispasmodic; diuretic, digestive; hypotensive. *Ext:* antirheumatic, vulnerary, anti-inflammatory. *Seas:* fresh leaves. Its aromatic oil, toxic when taken in large quantities, is used in the manufacture of perfumes.

Tilia platyphillos Scop.   Tiliaceae

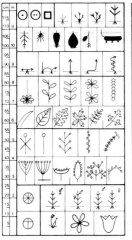

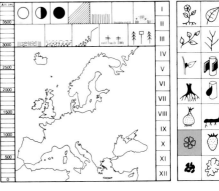

Properties: *Int:* bechic; sudorific; sedative (nervous system), narcotic, antispasmodic (flowers); choleretic (bark).

Sedum acre L.   Crassulaceae

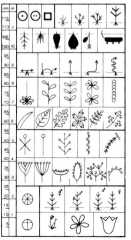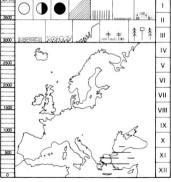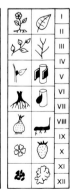

Properties: *Int:* hypotensive, anti-arthritic, abortive.

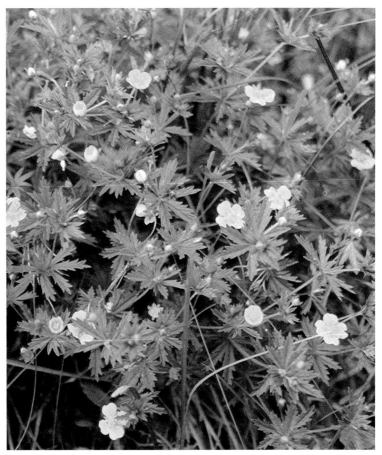

Potentilla erecta (L.) Rauschel   Rosaceae

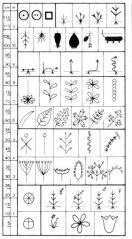

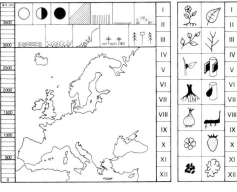

Properties: *Int:* astringent, stomachic, anti-inflammatory, antidiarrhoeic. *Ext:* vulnerary, cicatrizing and disinfectant. *Dye:* used only in former times for red leather.

Potentilla anserina L.   Rosaceae

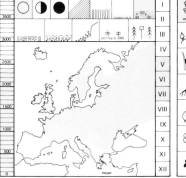

Properties: *Int:* astringent, stomachic, antispasmodic, antidiarrhoeic. *Ext:* vulnerary, anti-inflammatory. Eaten as a vegetable since antiquity (young leaves, roots).

Potentilla reptans L. Rosaceae

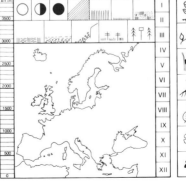

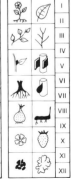

Properties: *Int:* astringent, antidiarrhoeic. *Ext:* anti-inflammatory, vulnerary.

Ranunculus ficaria L.   Ranunculaceae

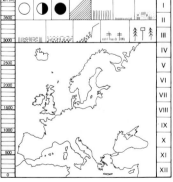
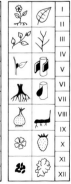

Properties: *Int.:* and *Ext.:* used as specific remedy for haemorrhoids. *Perf.:* emollient cosmetic. Boiled leaves can be eaten as substitute for spinach.

Caltha palustris L.

Ranunculaceae

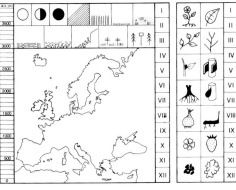

Properties: *Int:* (seldom used) sedative, antispasmodic, sudorific. Polyvalent remedy in homoeopathy.

Chelidonium majus L.   Papaveraceae

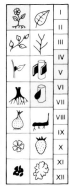

Properties: *Int:* (dangerous) antispasmodic, cholagogue, diuretic. *Ext:* antitumoral (warts). Its antimitotic properties make this a dangerous plant.

Iris pseudacorus L.   Iridaceae

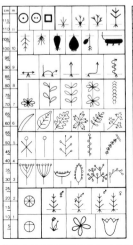

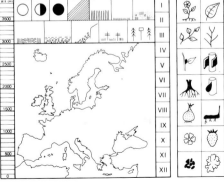

Properties: *Int:* strong astringent, powerful emetic, vermifuge, carminative, haemolytic (toxic in large doses). *Ext:*
rubefacient.

Cheiranthus cheiri L.   Cruciferae

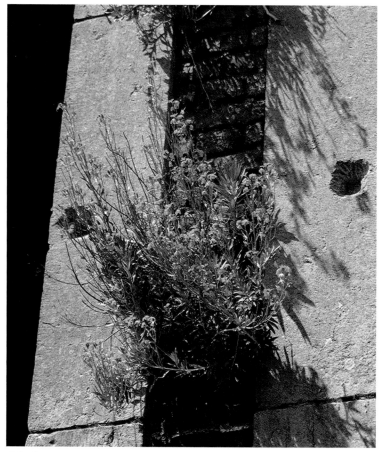

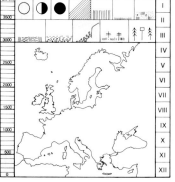
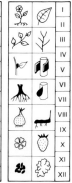

Properties: *Int:* diuretic, cardiotonic.

Arnica 43

Arnica montana L.   Compositae

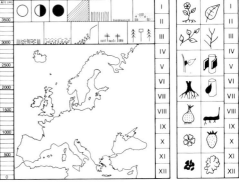

Properties *Int:* (dangerous) diuretic, cholagogue, hypotensive, antispasmodic. *Ext:* rubefacient, revulsive, antiecchymotic (bruises without wounds).

Inula helenium L.   Compositae

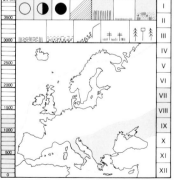

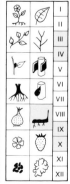

Properties: *Int:* aperitive and stomachic; anticatarrhal; bechic, tonic; diuretic and antidiarrhoeic; emmenagogue; vermifuge. *Ext:* antiseptic and antipruriginous. *Seas:* pickled rhizomes were once used as seasoning.

Anthyllis vulneraria L.

Papilionaceae

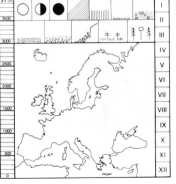

Properties: *Ext:* vulnerary, cicatrizing.

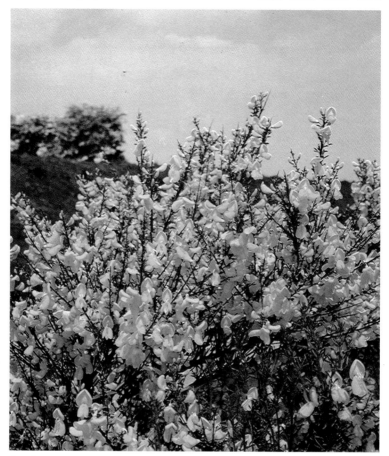

Cytisus scoparius (L.) Link   Papilionaceae

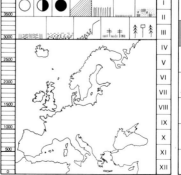
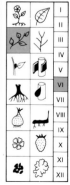

Properties: *Int:* Diuretic, antirheumatic; cardiotonic; hypertensive. *Ext:* poison antidote (application of ground branches). *Seas:* floral buds pickled in vinegar (in small quantities).

Primula veris L.   Primulaceae

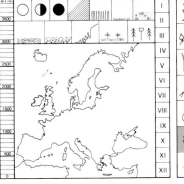

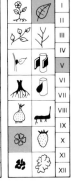

Properties: *Int:* essentially anticatarrhal and expectorant; diuretic; sedative; analgesic and antirheumatic. Young leaves can be eaten in salads.

Sinapis arvensis L.   Cruciferae

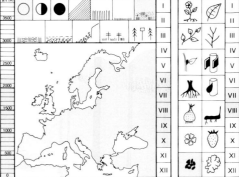

Properties: *Int:* laxative (whole grains). *Ext:* rubefacient (powdered). This species is a lot less active than white mustard (*Sinapis alba* L.), which is extensively cultivated and used to prepare French table mustard.

Hypericum perforatum L.

Guttiferae

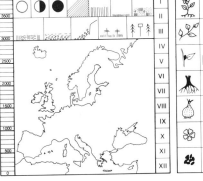

Properties: *Int:* sedative (spasmolytic), hypotensive, stomachic. *Ext:* excellent cicatrizer and antiseptic (wounds, haematomas, burns).

Senecio jacobaea L.   Compositae

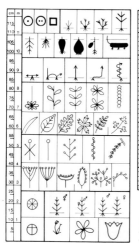

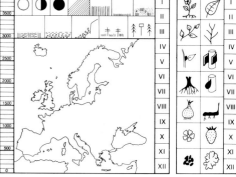

Properties: *Int:* emmenagogue, sedative; antimitotic, antitumoral although rather difficult to control and dangerous (cancerogenic).

Solidago virgaurea L.   Compositae

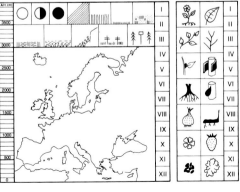

Properties: *Int:* astringent, diuretic and antidiarrhoeic. *Ext:* vulnerary, anti-inflammatory.

Tussilago farfara L.   Compositae

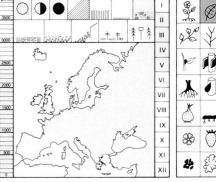

Properties: *Int:* bechic, expectorant; anticatarrhal; anti-asthmatic. *Ext:* resolutive. Can successfully be used as a substitute for tobacco.

Tanacetum vulgare L.   Compositae

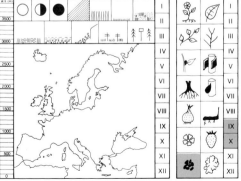

Properties: *Int:* Excellent vermifuge; aperitive, digestive; emmenagogue, abortive. *Ext:* revulsive, antirheumatic. Seeds can be used as seasoning as well as in the preparation of liqueurs (Benedictine) but the essence is however very toxic (convulsions, paralysis).

Santolina chamaecyparissus L.   Compositae

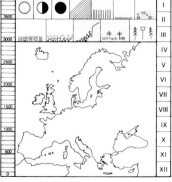

Properties: *Int:* vermifuge; tonic, antispasmodic.

Taraxacum vulgare Schrank   Compositae

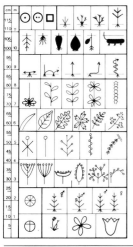

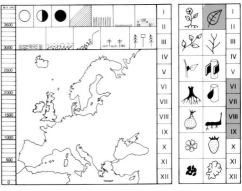

Properties: *Int:* aperitive, bitter-tonic. Essentially a chola-gogue and choleretic; stomachic; laxative. Depurative and diuretic (fresh young leaves). Excellent when eaten in salads.

Cnicus benedictus L.   Compositae

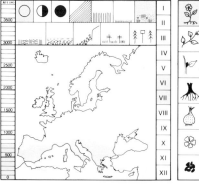

Properties: *Int:* bitter aperitive, stomach tonic, digestive; diuretic, uricolytic and depurative. In large doses also an emetic. *Ext:* detergent.

Hieracium pilosella L.   Compositae

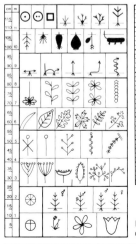

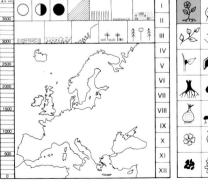

Properties: *Int:* astringent; diuretic, uricolytic, depurative; cholagogue. Antibiotic (brucellosis).

Melilotus officinalis (L.) Pallas   Papilionaceae

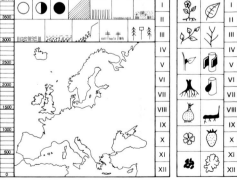

Properties: *Int:* antispasmodic (soothing, narcotic); antithrombotic; diuretic and antiseptic of the urinary ducts. *Ext:* antirheumatic, anti-inflammatory (conjunctivitis, styes, suppurations).

Agrimonia eupatoria L.

Rosaceae

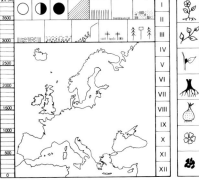

Properties: *Int:* astringent, decongestant (stomach, liver, gall-bladder), antidiarrhoeic. *Ext:* astringent, vulnerary; anti-inflammatory (mouth). *Dye:* causes wool to become golden yellow.

Geum urbanum L.   Rosaceae

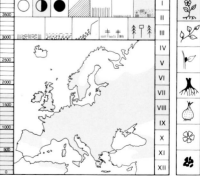

Properties: *Int:* astringent, stomach tonic, anti-inflammatory, antidiarrhoeic. *Ext:* vulnerary; antihaemorroidal; anti-inflammatory (mouth). *Seas:* rhizomes can be used as substitute for cloves; young leaves are edible in salads. *Dye:* orangy-brown to light-brown tones.

Gentiana lutea L.   Gentianaceae

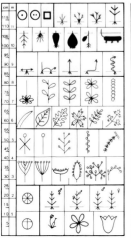

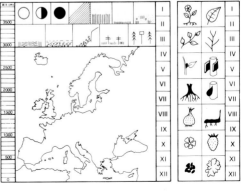

Properties: *Int:* bitter-tonic, stomachic, cholagogue and choleretic; febrifuge. Used as a basis for certain bitter aperitifs and liqueurs.

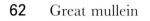

Verbascum thapsus L.   Scrophulariaceae

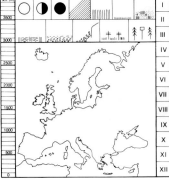

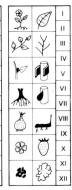

Properties: *Int:* (flowers) sedative; pectoral, antitussive; emollient (digestive and urinary ducts). *Ext:* (leaves used as emollient poultices) antihaemorrhoidal; cutaneous anti-inflammatory.

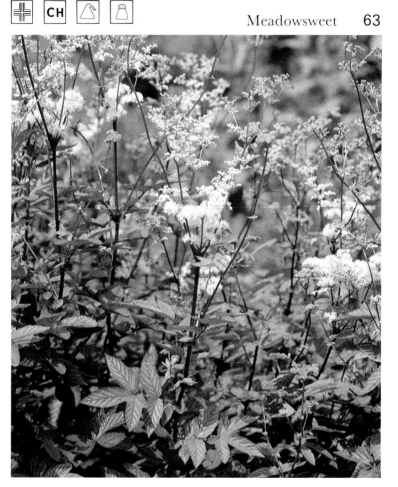

Filipendula ulmaria (L.) Maxim   Rosaceae

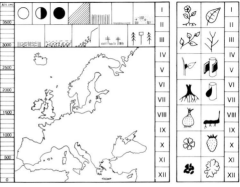

Properties: *Int:* excellent febrifuge (vegetal aspirin); sudorific; antirheumatic; diuretic (uricolytic); anti-arthritic; mild antispasmodic, sedative. The flowers give an agreeable scent to wine. *Dye:* deep yellow or green in combination with a mordant.

Laurus nobilis L.   Lauraceae

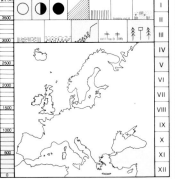

Properties: *Int:* stomach tonic, carminative, antiseptic. *Ext:* antirheumatic, parasiticide. *Seas:* only the leaves are used.

Frangula alnus Miller   Rhamnaceae

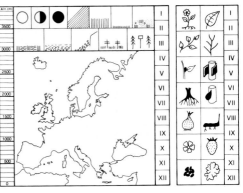

Properties: *Int:* (the fresh drug is very strong and vomitory; it should be allowed to age for at least a year or should be 'aged' by keeping it for a whole hour at 100°C/212°F), laxative or purgative according to dosage; cholagogue.

Euonymus europaeus L.   Celastraceae

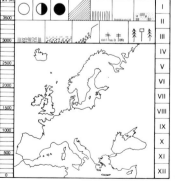

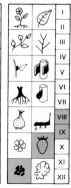

Properties: *Int:* to be altogether avoided as the bark is a strong emetic and the fruits are highly poisonous. *Ext:* parasiticide (lice and scab).

Bryonia cretica L.
ssp. **dioica** (Jacq.) Tutin

Cucurbitaceae

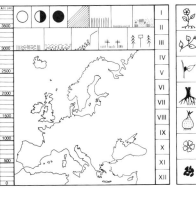

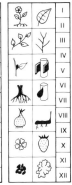

Properties: *Int:* to be avoided as a drastic purgative, emetic and abortive. *Ext:* powerful revulsive, anti-arthritic, anti-rheumatic, anti-ecchymotic.

Sambucus nigra L.   Caprifoliaceae

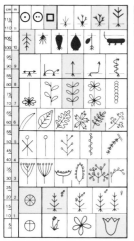

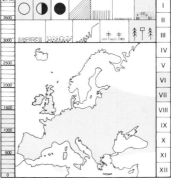

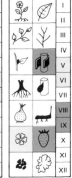

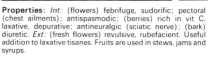

Properties: *Int:* (flowers) febrifuge, sudorific; pectoral (chest ailments); antispasmodic; (berries) rich in vit C, laxative, depurative; antineuralgic (sciatic nerve); (bark) diuretic. *Ext:* (fresh flowers) revulsive, rubefacient. Useful addition to laxative tisanes. Fruits are used in stews, jams and syrups.

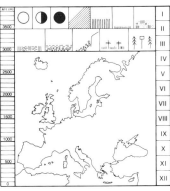

Peucedanum ostruthium (L.) Koch   Umbelliferae

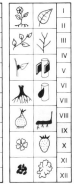

Properties: *Int:* bitter aromatic, aperitive, carminative; emollient, expectorant. *Ext:* anti-ecchymotic, vulnerary.

Heracleum sphondylium L.   Umbelliferae

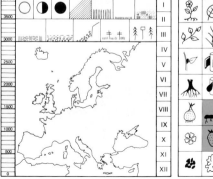

Properties: *Int:* (fruits) hypotensive; (leaves and rhizomes) sedative, anti-anxiety; stomach tonic; aphrodisiac. In the old days, a kind of ale was prepared by fermenting leaves and stems.

Daucus carota L.   Umbelliferae

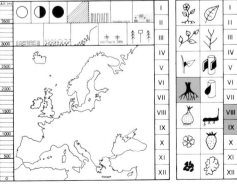

Properties: *Int:* (root) biocatalyst (high level of vit A, B$_1$, B$_2$, C), diuretic, depurative, antidiarrhoeic; (fruits) diuretic, carminative, galactagogue, vermifuge. *Ext:* (root pulp) antihaemorragic, cicatrizing, antipruriginous.

Conyzia canadensis (L.) Cronq.   Compositae

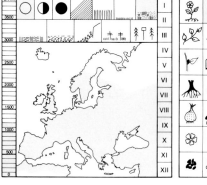

Properties: *Int:* astringent, antidiarrhoeic, haemostatic; diuretic and antirheumatic.

Polygonum aviculare L.   Polygonaceae

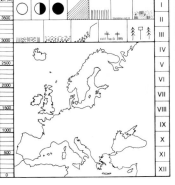

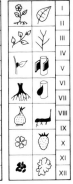

Properties: *Int:* astringent, excellent antidiarrhoeic; haemostatic; remineralizing. *Ext:* vulnerary, cicatrizing.

Marrubium vulgare L.   Labiatae

Properties: *Int:* above all a bechic and expectorant; cholagogue; bitter stomach tonic; febrifuge; cardiotonic (extrasystole). *Ext:* antiseptic, antipruriginous.

Lamium album L. Labiatae

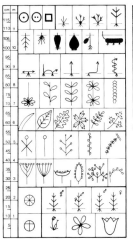

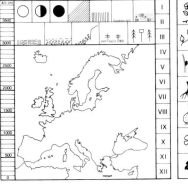

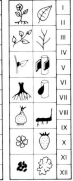

Properties: *Int:* astringent, antidiarrhoeic, haemostatic (leucorrhea, metrorragia, haemorrhoids); sudorific, diuretic. *Ext:* haemostatic (small wounds).

Crataegus monogyna Jacq.   Rosaceae

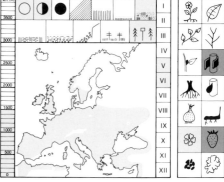

Properties: *Int:* hypotensive, cardiotonic, sedative, antispasmodic (flowers); astringent, antidiarrhoeic, antiscorbutic (fruits); febrifuge (bark). The haws are excellent in jams.

Prunus spinosa L.   Rosaceae

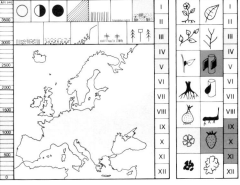

Properties: *Int:* diuretic, laxative (mild), sudorific (flowers); astringent, antidiarrhoeic, biocatalyst (vit C), stomach tonic (fruits, above all when green); febrifuge (bark). The sloes are used in the preparation of liqueurs (sloe gin).

Fragaria vesca L.   Rosaceae

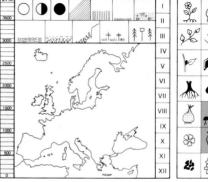

Properties: *Int:* diuretic, depurative; astringent and antidiarrhoeic, antirheumatic (leaves and rhizomes); re-mineralizing, diuretic, antilithiasic, hypotensive (fruits). *Ext:* vulnerary.

⊞ CH △ ⬒

Rubus fruticosus L.   Rosaceae

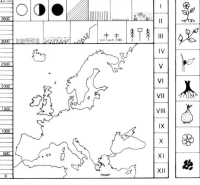

Properties: *Int:* astringent, antidiarrhoeic (leaves); diuretic, antiscorbutic (fruits). *Ext:* vulnerary, anti-inflammatory (leaves).

Cistus ladanifer L.   Cistaceae

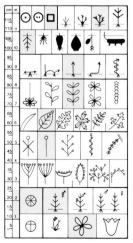

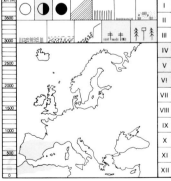

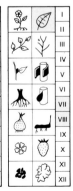

Properties: *Int:* astringent, antidiarrhoeic; antispasmodic. *Ext:* vulnerary, antiseptic. *Perf:* the resin exuded by leaves and branches is concentrated and moulded into perfumed balls.

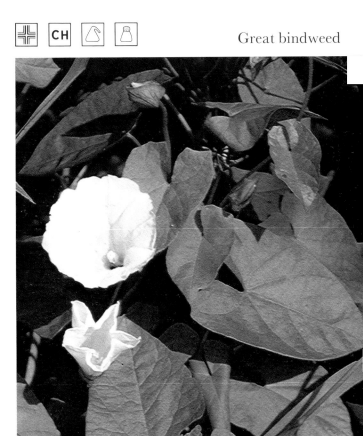

Calystegia sepium (L.) R. Br.   Convolvulaceae

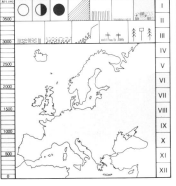

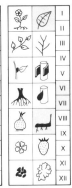

Properties: *Int:* purgative.

Allium ursinum L.   Liliaceae

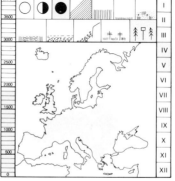

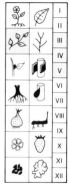

Properties: *Int:* (fresh plant) depurative, antiseptic (intestines), vermifuge, diuretic, cholagogue, hypotensive, biocatalyst. *Ext:* rubefacient.

Viburnum opulus L.   Caprifoliaceae

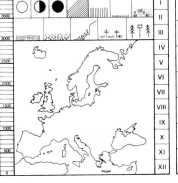

Properties: *Int:* astringent; diuretic; antispasmodic, uterine sedative. *Seas:* fruits can be stewed (they are poisonous when fresh).

Galium odoratum (L.) Scop.   Rubiaceae

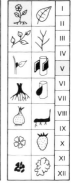

Properties: *Int:* sedative, antispasmodic, narcotic; chola-gogue; digestive, tonic, diuretic. Fermented in sweet white wine it produces a drink called 'Maitrank' (May wine).

Bellis perennis L.   Compositae

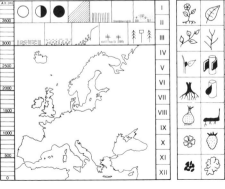

Properties: *Int:* expectorant, depurative, sudorific, tonic. *Ext:* vulnerary (anti-ecchymotic), anti-inflammatory. The young leaves can be added to salads and soups in small quantities.

Chamomilla recutita (L.) Rauschert   Compositae

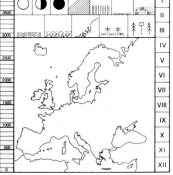

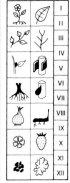

Properties: *Int:* stomachic, sedative, antispasmodic; carminative; sudorific; emmenagogue. *Ext:* anti-inflammatory (haemorrhoids), ophthalmic.

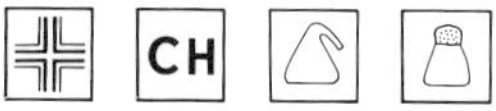

Tanacetum parthenium (L.) Schultz Bip. Compositae

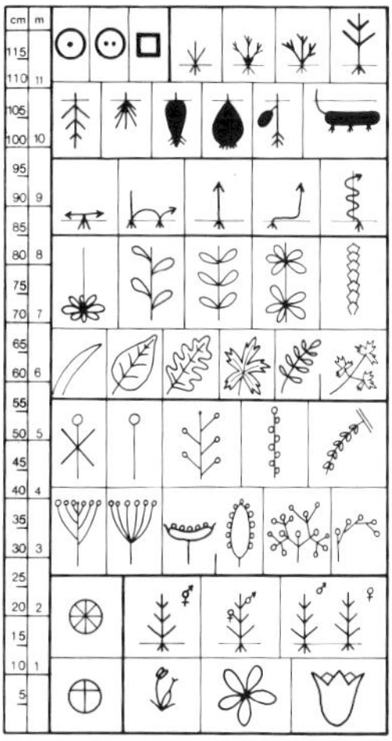

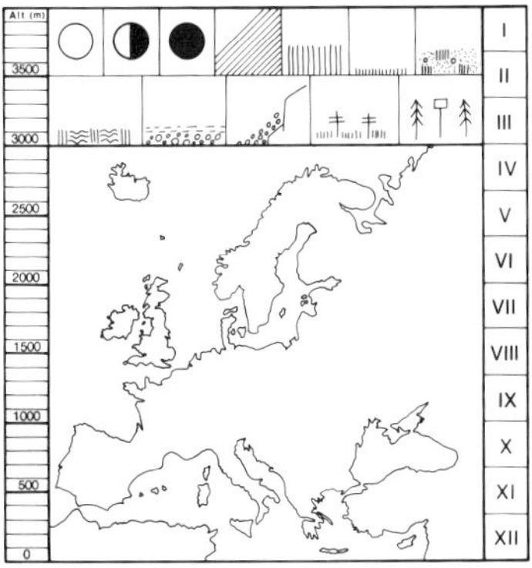

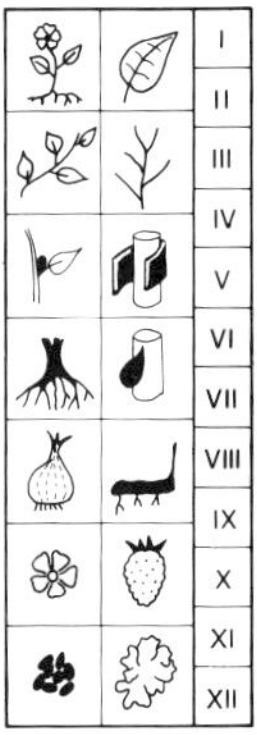

Properties: *Int:* antispasmodic, emmenagogue, febrifuge. Insecticide (like its relative pyrethrum).

Capsella bursa pastoris (L.) Medicus   Cruciferae

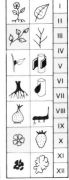

Properties: *Int:* astringent tonic; haemostatic (metrorragies, nose bleeds). The young plants can be eaten in salads or cooked in soups.

Alliaria petiolata (Bieb.) Cavara and Grande   Cruciferae

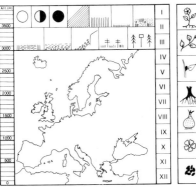

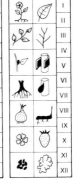

Properties: *Int:* diuretic, antiscorbutic, expectorant. *Ext:* vulnerary, antiseptic. The flowers and young leaves can be added to salads instead of garlic.

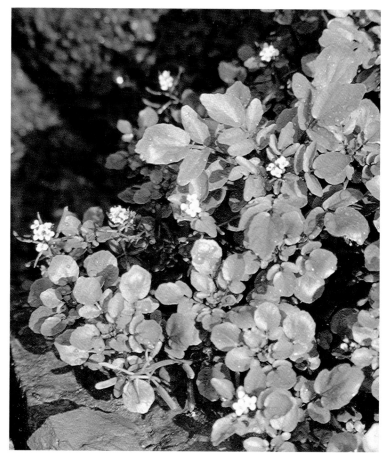

Nasturtium officinale R. Br.   Cruciferae

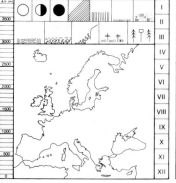

Properties: *Int:* tonic, anti-anaemic, antiscorbutic; diuretic and depurative; bechic and expectorant. *Ext:* resolutive.

Satureia montana L.   Labiatae

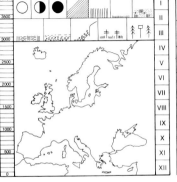

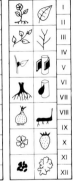

Properties: *Int:* antiseptic; tonic, stimulant of the stomach, carminative; expectorant; aphrodisiac. *Ext:* fungicide. *Seas:* one of the most important culinary herbs.

Rosa canina L.

Rosaceae

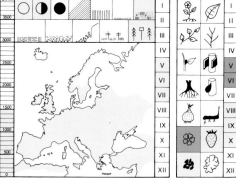

Properties: *Int:* (fruits) anti-anaemic and antiscorbutic (rich in vitamins, particularly vit C), astringent, antidiarrhoeic; (seeds) diuretic; (flowers) laxative. *Ext:* (leaves) cicatrizing. Excellent jam can be made with the fruits.

Angelica sylvestris L.   Umbelliferae

 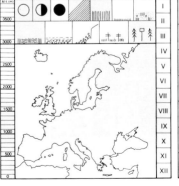 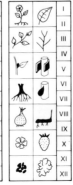

Properties: *Int:* stomach tonic, carminative, antiseptic.

Achillea millefolium L.   Compositae

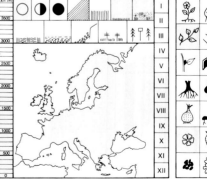

Properties: *Int.:* bitter tonic, carminative, vermifuge, spasmolytic; emmenagogue; expectorant; antiseptic. *Ext:* cicatrizing (antihaemorrhoidal).

Menyanthes trifoliata L.   Menyanthaceae

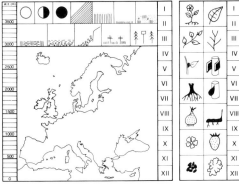

Properties: *Int:* antiscorbutic; aperitive, tonic, depurative; febrifuge; emmenagogue.

Vaccinium vitis-idaea L.   Ericaceae

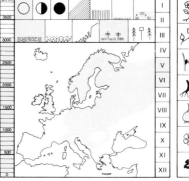

Properties: *Int:* (leaves) astringent, diuretic, antiseptic of the urinary ducts; (fruits) antidiarrhoeic. The berries are excellent both in jams and stewed.

Oxalis acetosella L.   Oxalidaceae

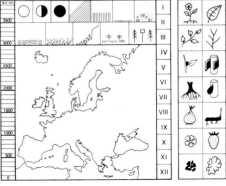

Properties: *Int:* (fresh plants) refreshing, stomachic, diuretic. *Ext:* anti-inflammatory. *Seas:* can be used in small quantities in salads and soups (see also common sorrel, pl 2).

Thymus vulgaris L.   Labiatae

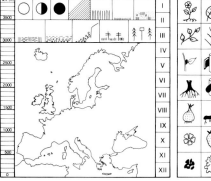

Properties: *Int:* tonic, stomachic, carminative, antispasmodic; sudorific; antiseptic and vermifuge; balsamic, expectorant. *Ext:* antiseptic, antirheumatic. *Seas:* the most widely used of all aromatic herbs.

Valeriana repens Host.   Valerianaceae

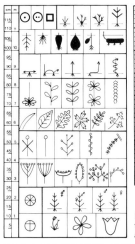

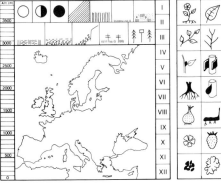

Properties: *Int:* antispasmodic, anticonvulsive, sedative of the nervous system; stomachic, mildly narcotic; anti-asthmatic.

Saponaria officinalis L.   Caryophyllaceae

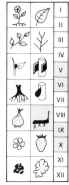

Properties: *Int:* depurative, diuretic, sudorific, cholagogue, expectorant. *Ext:* effective against skin diseases. Can be used instead of soap (shampoo).

Eupatorium cannabinum L.   Compositae

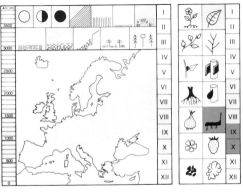

Properties: *Int:* aperitive, stimulant; laxative, depurative and antirheumatic; choleretic. *Ext:* cicatrizing (fresh leaves).

Althaea officinalis L.   Malvaceae

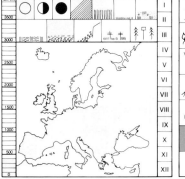

Properties: *Int:* emollient, anti-inflammatory; laxative; bechic (mild). *Ext:* sedative, anti-inflammatory.

Ballota nigra L.　　　　Labiatae

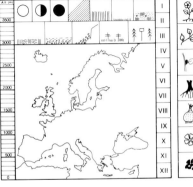

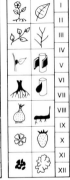

Properties: *Int*: sedative, antispasmodic; choleric; hypotensive. *Ext*: detergent.

Leonorus cardiaca L.   Labiatae

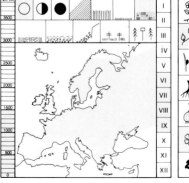

Properties: *Int:* sedative, antispasmodic; emmenagogue; antidiarrhoeic. *Ext:* vulnerary.

Origanum vulgare L.　　　　　　　　　　Labiatae

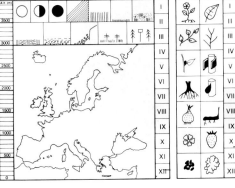

Properties: *Int:* antispasmodic, stomachic, tonic; carminative; antiseptic; bechic, expectorant. *Dye:* imparts reddish-brown tones to wool.

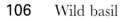

Clinopodium vulgare L.   Labiatae

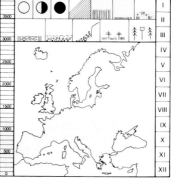

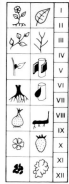

Properties: *Int:* tonic, stomachic, expectorant. *Seas:* imparts a distinctive flavour. Much cultivated.

Salvia sclarea L.   Labiatae

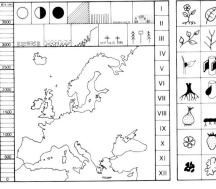

Properties: *Int:* stomach stimulant, antispasmodic; anti-sudorific, emmenagogue. *Ext:* cicatrizing. *Perf:* perfume fixative. *Seas:* has a sharper taste than sage (*Salvia officinalis*, pl 143).

Salvia pratensis L.   Labiatae

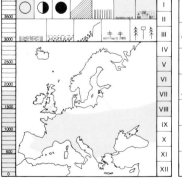

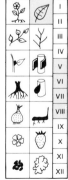

Properties: similar to those of sage (*Salvia officinalis*, pl 143) but much milder. *Int:* bitter tonic, stomachic, antispasmodic, antisudorific. *Ext:* astringent.

Thymus pulegioides L.   Labiatae

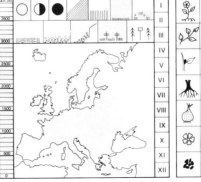

Properties: *Int:* bitter tonic, stomachic, antispasmodic; carminative; vermifuge; expectorant and sedative of the respiratory ducts. *Ext:* vulnerary. *Seas:* a substitute for cultivated thyme.

Geranium robertianum L.   Geraniaceae

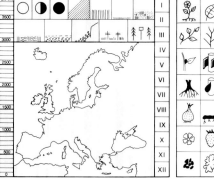

Properties: *Int:* astringent, antidiarrhoeic; antispasmodic; diuretic (mild). *Ext:* anti-inflammatory (ophthalmia, skin infections).

Polygonum bistorta L.   Polygonaceae

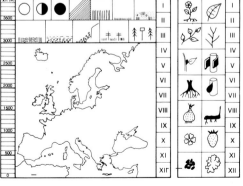

Properties: *Int:* astringent tonic, antidiarrhoeic, anti-inflammatory. *Ext:* vulnerary, anti-inflammatory (mouth infections, aphtae), antihaemorrhoidal. The young leaves can be used in salads or cooked like spinach.

Centaurium erythraea Rafn.   Gentianaceae

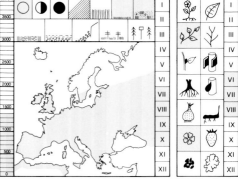

Properties: *Int:* bitter tonic, aperitif, stomachic, sedative of the digestive duct; choleric; carminative; febrifuge. *Ext:* anti-ecchymotic. The bitter principle is used in the preparation of liqueurs.

Fumaria officinalis L.   Papaveraceae

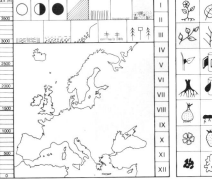

Properties: *Int:* aperitive, stomach tonic, hypertensive (at the beginning of a treatment); antiscorbutic; depurative, antiplethoric. *Ext:* used to treat several skin afflictions.

Malva sylvestris L.   Malvaceae

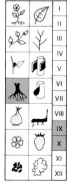

Properties: *Int:* emollient, bechic (similar to marsh mallow, pl 102); laxative (flowers and leaves). *Ext:* anti-inflammatory, used against skin irritations and abscesses (leaves and roots).

Digitalis purpurea L.   Scrophulariacae

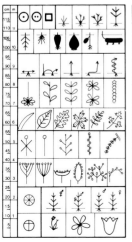

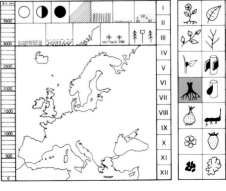

Properties: (toxic and dangerous) source of valuable glycoside Digitoxin which acts on heart muscles. Dried plant known as 'digitalis'. Not to be gathered by amateurs.

Sanguisorba minor Scop.   Rosaceae

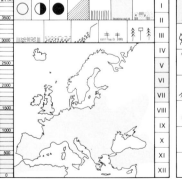

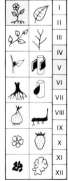

Properties: *Int:* astringent, haemostatic; digestive; carminative; diuretic. *Ext:* vulnerary. The young leaves can be used in salads or vegetable soups.

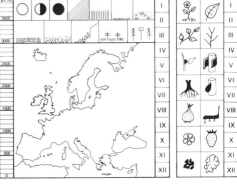

Calluna vulgaris (L.) Hull   Ericaceae

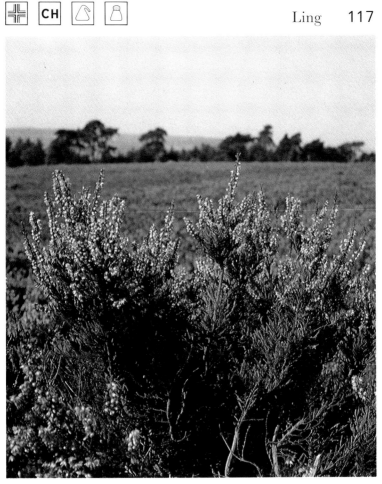

Properties: *Int:* powerful diuretic, antiseptic and sedative of the urinary ducts; depurative; astringent, antidiarrhoeic and antirheumatic.

Vaccinium myrtillus L.

Ericaceae

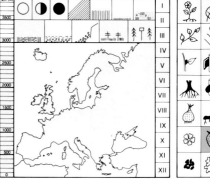

Properties: *Int:* astringent, antidiarrhoeic, antiseptic (fruits); hypoglycemic (leaves). *Ext:* anti-inflammatory (stomatitis, aphtae).

Allium schoenoprasum L.   Liliaceae

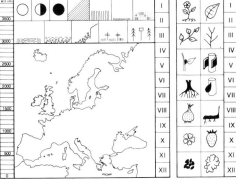

Properties: *Int:* similar to those of garlic and onion, for which it is a useful substitute (antiscorbutic, antiseptic, revulsive, hypoglycemiant). *Seas:* very widely used due to the mildness and subtlety of its aroma.

Centranthus ruber (L.) DC.   Valerianaceae

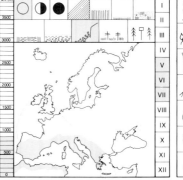

Properties: *Int:* sedative of the central nervous system, antispasmodic, anticonvulsive (same properties as pl 99).

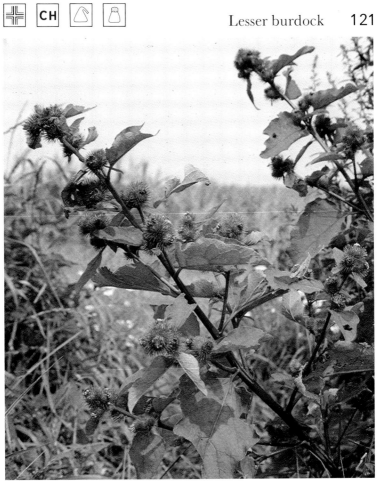

Arctium minus (Hill) Bernh.   Compositae

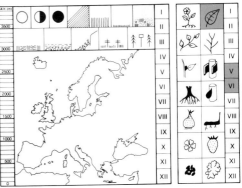

Properties: *Int:* antibiotic; choleretic; diuretic, depurative (root). *Ext:* antibiotic; extremely efficient drug in the treatment of skin afflictions (boils, dermatitis, acne), antirheumatic. The root can be eaten as a vegetable (substitute for salsifies).

Lythrum salicaria L.

Lythraceae

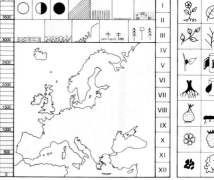

Properties: *Int:* astringent, antidiarrhoeic, haemostatic, mildly antibiotic. *Ext:* antipruriginous. Once used for tanning due to its high content of tannin.

Rhododendron ferrugineum L.

Ericaceae

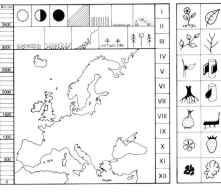

Properties: *Int:* anti-arthritic, antilithiasic, antineuralgic.

Papaver rhoeas L.   Papaveraceae

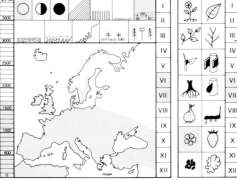

Properties: *Int:* light narcotic, antispasmodic; sudorific; pectoral, soothing, emollient, sedative (coughs). *Ext:* anti-inflammatory (ophthalmia). The seeds can be used instead of those of the garden poppy (pastry cooking).

Pistacia terebinthus L.   Anacardiaceae

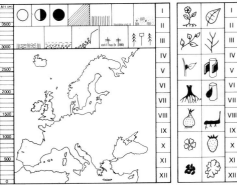

Properties: the resin oozing from cuts in the bark is used to prepare unguents and poultices.

Verbena officinalis L.   Verbenaceae

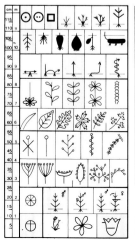

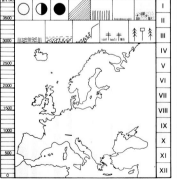

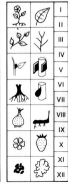

Properties: *Int:* astringent, antidiarrhoeic; stomachic stimulant; emmanagogue; antineuralgic and antirheumatic. *Ext:* vulnerary, anti-ecchymotic.

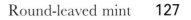

Mentha suaveolens Ehrh.   Labiatae

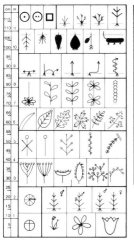

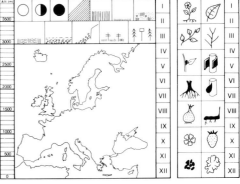

Properties: *Int:* tonic, refreshing, digestive, antispasmodic; cholagogue; antiseptic (menthol, dangerous for the nervous system). *Seas:* exactly the same use as for peppermint.

Mentha aquatica L.   Labiatae

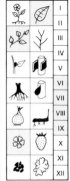

Properties: *Int:* stomach tonic, antispasmodic (cramps); analgesic; cholagogue; carminative. *Perf:* baths, linen.

Dipsacus fullonum L.   Dipsacaceae

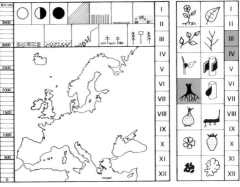

Properties: *Int:* (root) aperitive, depurative, skin afflictions; (flowering plant) skin afflictions (homoeopathy). The capitula of a related species in cultivation were used to card certain fibres.

Rosmarinus officinalis L.   Labiatae

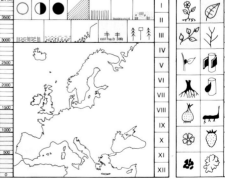

Properties: *Int:* tonic, stomach stimulant, antispasmodic; carminative; cholagogue; emmenagogue. *Ext:* antiseptic, anti-ecchymotic and antirheumatic. *Seas:* excellent aromatic herb. *Perf:* lotions, oils, scented waters, shampoos.

Glycyrrhizia glabra L.   Papilionaceae

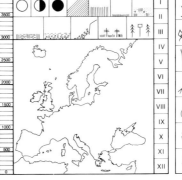

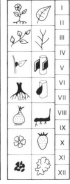

Properties: *Int:* refreshing, soothing, pectoral, expectorant; stomach sedative, antispasmodic; diuretic. *Ext:* anti-inflammatory.

Cardamine pratensis L.   Cruciferae

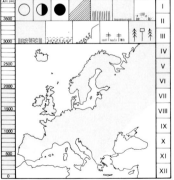

Properties: *Int:* tonic, antiscorbutic; expectorant, bechic; diuretic. The young leaves can be used in salads.

Symphytum asperum Lepechin   Boraginaceae

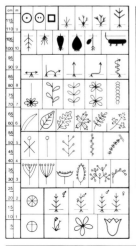

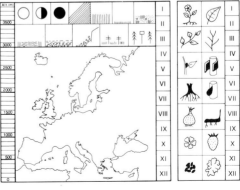

Properties: *Int:* astringent, emollient, bechic. *Ext:* cicatrizing, sedative, anti-inflammatory.

Centaurea montana L.   Compositae

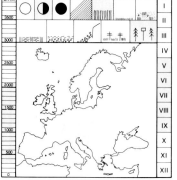

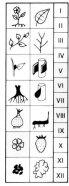

Properties: *Int:* astringent, diuretic, digestive. *Ext:* sedative, anti-inflammatory, (ophthalmia) like the field cornflower.

Viola tricolor L.   Violaceae

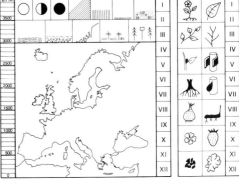

Properties: *Int:* expectorant; diuretic; depurative and slightly laxative; febrifuge and sudorific. *Ext:* used as depurative against skin troubles (acne, eczema).

Solanum dulcamara L.   Solanaceae

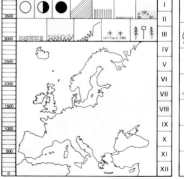

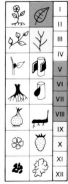

Properties: *Int:* depurative, antiplethoric, diuretic, anti-rheumatic (stems). *Ext:* used to treat skin troubles and haemorrhoids (leaves).

Borago officinalis L.   Boraginaceae

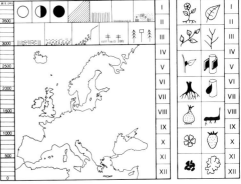

Properties: *Int:* emollient, pectoral (flowers); depurative, sudorific, diuretic, chlorurolytic, antirheumatic (leaves and stems). *Seas:* young leaves pickled in vinegar. The leaves were once eaten as vegetables.

Vinca minor L.   Apocynaceae

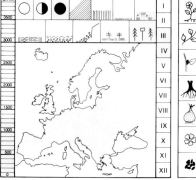

Properties: *Int:* bitter tonic; hypoglycemic (antidiabetic); astringent, antihaemorrhagic; hypotensive, vaso-dilating. *Ext:* vulnerary, anti-ecchymotic. Extracts are used to treat leukaemia.

Veronica chamaedrys L.   Scrophulariaceae

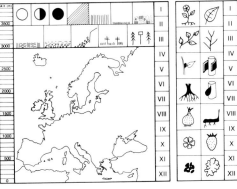

Properties: similar to those of the heath speedwell (*Veronica officinalis*): *Int*: astringent, stomach tonic; bechic. *Ext*: cicatrizing.

Cichorium intybus L.   Compositae

Properties: *Int:* bitter tonic, refreshing, stomachic; chola-gogue, depurative; hypoglycemic; diuretic. The young leaves are eaten in salads; the roasted root is added to, or substituted for, coffee.

Glechoma hederacea L.   Labiatae

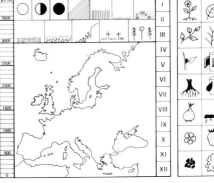

Properties: *Int:* bechic, antispasmodic, tonic of the respiratory ducts. *Ext:* vulnerary, cicatrizing (abscesses, boils). *Seas:* fresh or dried leaves.

Lavandula angustifolia Miller   Labiatae

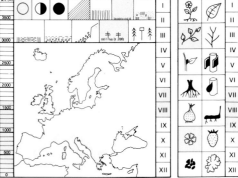

Properties: *Int:* stomachic, antispasmodic; diuretic, sudorific. *Ext:* vulnerary, antiseptic; antirheumatic, anti-ecchymotic (as a liniment). *Seas:* in very small doses! *Perf:* as a corrective; in scented waters. Insecticide.

Salvia officinalis L.   Labiatae

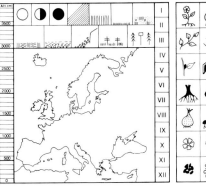

Properties: *Int:* antisudorific; emmenagogue and oestrogenic; stomach tonic; antispasmodic, choleretic; hypoglycemic. *Ext:* antiseptic, cicatrizing. *Seas:* fresh or dried leaves. Also used in perfumes and liqueurs.

Hyssopus officinalis L.   Labiatae

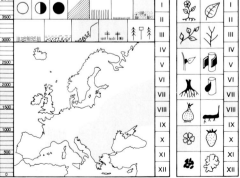

Properties: *Int:* astringent, aperitive, digestive; bechic, expectorant (the aromatic oil is a convulsive). *Ext:* vulnerary, cicatrizing, anti-ecchymotic. *Seas:* fresh or dried young leaves. The essence is used in the preparation of liqueurs (aperitifs).

APPENDIX I

Botanical notes

The species descriptions on the previous pages contain information in a highly condensed form. Despite this style, some details have had to be omitted from the plate pages for reasons of space; these aspects include certain structural or functional peculiarities, some ecological and habitat preferences, or indeed some important synonyms. These further details are gathered in this appendix: the numbers correspond to those of the plates for easy reference. Other questions are also answered: how one can distinguish a newly-picked herb from a similar one; whether there are one or more related species with similar properties.

1. **Monk's rhubarb**
The plant is similar to common rhubarb and belongs to the same family. It is a nitrophyte growing in thick clusters. In the Alps, its leaves are used to wrap fresh butter and the rhizomes are one of the ingredients of pig feed.

2. **Common sorrel**
The garden sorrel (*Rumex rugosus* Campd.), the origin of which is unknown, has larger lower leaves of a paler green.

3. **Water-pepper**
A knotgrass very easy to distinguish from the other species of the genus by its lax cluster of flowers clearly separated and by its acrid, peppery taste.

4. **Pellitory-of-the-wall**
Syn: Parietaria judaica L., *P. ramiflora* Moench

5. **Ribwort plantain**
Other plantains have the same properties, particularly the hoary plantain (*Plantago media* L.) and the greater plantain (*Plantago major* L.); both have elliptical leaves, a flower stalk without grooves, smooth or slightly lined. The leaves of the hoary plantain have a petiole decidedly shorter than the limb; those of the ratstail a petiole of almost the same length as the limb.

6. **Mugwort**
It belongs to the same genus as the wormwood (pl 27), which can be easily identified by the whitish colour of its leaves (due to their thick

coating of hairy fur). The other members of the genus have leaves with linear segments no wider than 1mm (c $^1/_{16}$ in).

7. Sweet vernal grass
The inflorescence resembles a cluster but is in fact a contracted panicle. When dry, the plant smells strongly of coumarin, which contributes to the sweet smell of hay.

8. Common nettle
The annual nettle (*Urtica urens*) is also a stinging one and with the same properties; it is a monoecious, with flowers growing in simple clusters.

9. Common polypody
Similar in taste to the liquorice (pl 131).

10. Hart's-tongue
Syn: Asplenium scolopendrium L.

11. Male fern
Both the beginner and the expert have some difficulty in differentiating the male fern from other ferns growing in the same habitats, particularly from the lady fern, which is no more female than the other is male.

12. Horsetail
Only the sterile stem is shown in the photograph, as this is the part to pick. In spring a brownish stem grows from the same rhizome; this stem, apparently devoid of chlorophyll, carries on its tip a spore-bearing head.

13. Prickly juniper
This juniper is characterized by its needles which present, on the underside, two white stripes either side of the nerve, while the common juniper (pl 14) only has one. Cade oil, as it is known, is extracted from the wood when partly burned, and is used in various pomades.

14. Common juniper
In the autumn following fertilization, the juniper produces small fleshy cones, first green then bluish, often called 'juniper berries'. Botanically speaking, they are not berries at all, nor fruits, because the juniper is a gymnosperm, ie a plant producing naked seeds (not enclosed in an ovary).

15. Scots pine
Other pine species have the same properties: maritime pine (*Pinus pinaster* Aiton), stone pine (*Pinus pinea* L.), Austrian pine (*Pinus nigra* Arn.). All three have needles grouped in pairs but the former two have the longest needles of all (10–20cm, c 4–8in), while the Austrian pine's needles grow to 7–12 cm (c 2$^3/_4$–4$^3/_4$in) and the Scots pine's to 4–6cm (c 1$^1/_2$–2$^1/_2$in). The habitat of the Scots pine has progressively diminished compared with what it was in prehistoric times: the map shows the European areas where it is indigenous and, circled by a broken line, those where it could be.

16. **Couchgrass**
Syn: Agropyron repens (L) Beauv., *Elytrigia repens* (L.) Nevski
Quite different from Bermuda grass (*Cynodon dactylon* (L.) Pers) whose inflorescence is composed of several clusters giving it the appearance of fingers.

17. **Sea buckthorn**
Several sub-species, all different in their habitat and ecology (dunes, banks of mountain streams); the subspecies of the coastlines is often planted to anchor dunes, where it forms impenetrable thickets.

18. **Glasswort** (or Saltwort)
Grouped under this name (*Salicornia europaea* L.) are several closely-related species difficult to separate; in order to study them, one needs specimens complete with flowers. The flowers are grouped in small cymes of three, forming a false cluster.

19. **Downy birch**
The photograph shows the male catkins and, on the left partly hidden, a female one. The downy birch is very similar to the silver birch (*Betula pendula* Roth) and often mistaken for it. It differs from it in the more marked hairiness of the buds and young branches and the absence on these of the small warts which make the silver birch rough to the touch.

20. **Common alder**
The photograph shows a branch with empty cones (fruits of the previous year) and, towards the top, the young female cones. The shape of the leaf is typical and distinguishes this alder from other European species of the same genus.

21. **Sessile** (or Durmast) **oak**
Syn: Quercus sessilis
The English oak (*Q. robur* L., *syn: Q. pedunculata* Ehrh) differs from the sessile oak in that its leaves, which have very short petioles (it is the acorns which have a stem!), are wider at the tip and provided with small ear-like lobes at the base. The leaves of the sessile oak are wider in the middle and have no ear-like lobes. The photograph shows only the catkins of the male flowers.

   For medicinal use, only the young smooth bark should be gathered (without damaging the tree); for internal use, pick the leaves, which are less sharp.

22. **Ash**
It has naked flowers, generally hermaphrodite, each composed of two stamens and one pistil, grouped in lateral panicles along the branches of the mature tree. The photograph was taken when the fruits were beginning to form.

23. **Dog's mercury**
The photograph shows a colony of female plants with flowers and fruits; male plants are however more frequent and grow in larger colonies than the females, with which they do not seem to mix. The plant can be dangerous if used internally.

24. Common buckthorn

The female inflorescence is a very compact cyme in the shape of a small cone; the male one is less condensed and forms a panicle (in the photograph). Only the young female flowers are naked, the male ones having a floral involucre. It is possible to mistake the buckthorn for the alder buckthorn: however, the leaves of the latter are alternated and without indentations, the flowers hermaphrodite and the old branches never thorny.

25. Hops

The newly-ripened female cones (the only ones in the photograph) have certain glands on their bracts which, once detached, form the drug lupulin, a golden-yellow powder. The drug contains a complex aromatic oil which gives beer its taste and is used to perfume Cologne water. The plant's present European distribution is probably strongly influenced by man, as the original area was likely to be limited to the southern part of the area shown in the map.

26. Rock samphire

No additional information.

27. Wormwood

The distribution illustrated has been exaggerated; in many areas wormwood has probably naturalized as a result of cultivation.

28. Birthwort

Its geographical distribution is as difficult to establish as that of the wormwood. Probably indigenous to the Mediterranean basin, it spread north with ancient cultivations and settled there sporadically.

29. Lady's bedstraw

No additional information.

30. Fennel

A widely-known plant; the sweet fennel is a variety (*var. azoricum* (Mill.) Thell.) cultivated as a vegetable: the fleshy bases of the stalks grow into a bulb which can be eaten raw or cooked.

31. Common lady's-mantle

Today there is a great number of sub-species once grouped under the name of *Alchemilla vulgaris* L. This general treatment is kept in order to simplify the presentation, as many of these sub-species are very difficult to distinguish; the more widely-spread and easier to recognize include *Alchemilla xanthochlora* Rothm. (in the photograph).

32. Rue (or Herb of grace)

In cultivation the plant appears as a more luxuriant species known as *Ruta hortensis* Mill. This form does not present, however, any characteristics which might distinguish it from the wild form; some think the former has a stronger aroma, others believe the latter has more interesting properties.

33. Large-leaved lime

Has the same properties as the small-leaved lime (*Tilia cordata* Mill.) but is distinguished by the larger leaves as well as by the tufts of white hairs (instead of red) along the veins on the underside of the leaves. The hybrid of the two species (*Tilia × vulgaris* Hayne) is often planted and is also medicinal.

34. **Biting stonecrop** (or Wallpepper)

35. **Tormentil**
Syn: Potentilla tormentilla Stokes
It differs from the other members of the *Potentillae* with erect stems in the number of its petals – 4 instead of 5.

36. **Silverweed**
One often comes across a variety with leaves which are silvery on the upper side.

37. **Creeping cinquefoil** (or Five-leaved grass)

38. **Lesser celandine** (or Pilewort)
Syn: Ficaria ranunculoides Roth.
Many sub-species are known, among them *ssp. bulbifer* Lawalree which has bulbils on the axil of the leaves but is not very fertile.

39. **Marsh marigold**
No additional information.

40. **Greater celandine**
No additional information.

41. **Yellow flag**
No additional information.

42. **Wallflower**
Ornamental cultivation has brought this plant from south-east Europe into a great part of the continent, where it has naturalized in places. Naturalized stocks have golden-yellow flowers, while the cultivated ones vary in colour: yellow-orange, brownish-yellow, purple.

43. **Arnica** (or Mountain tobacco, Leopard's bane)
The plant can be recognized by its penetrating smell; in its own habitat it is the only one of the *Compositae* to have opposed leaves, as a rosette at the base. It is a strict calcifuge, avoided by cattle because of its toxicity but useful as a substitute for tobacco.

44. **Elecampane**
Native of south-east Europe, for centuries it has been cultivated as a medicinal herb and is now naturalized almost throughout Europe.

45. **Kidney vetch**
Makes good cattle fodder. It is a variable plant, more than twenty sub-species being known, including some varieties very difficult to identify.

46. **Broom**
Syn: Sarothamnus scoparius (L.) Wimm.
One should be careful not to confuse this broom with other members

of the *Papilionaceae* such as the gorse, which is thorny, or the Spanish broom (*Spartium junceum* L.). The latter is actually even more toxic: it is a Mediterranean species spreading north as far as southern France.

47. **Cowslip**
Syn: Primula officinalis (L.) Hill
The oxlip (*P. elatior* (L.) Hill) is sometimes used as a substitute; despite its name, it is not a larger plant and differs in its corolla, which is flat, pale yellow and has no smell, while the one of the cowslip is concave, golden yellow and perfumed.

48. **Charlock** (or Wild mustard)
Probably native of the Near East, sometimes difficult to distinguish from the white mustard (*Sinapis alba* L.); the leaves of the latter are deeply indented, while those of the former have less pronounced, pointed indentations. The black mustard (*Brassica nigra* (L.) Koch) also has simply-dented leaves, but the indentations are obtuse; this species is smooth, or with very few hairs, and the fruits appear along the axis of the inflorescence. Finally, the wild radish (*Raphanus raphanistrum* L.) has scanty fruits, flowers of variable colour and deeply-cut leaves, like those of the white mustard.

49. **Perforate St John's-wort**
Its inflorescence is not a cyme but a panicle.

50. **Common ragwort**
Like all *Senecio* members this herb contains alkaloids, toxic to the liver, and must be regarded as dangerous.

51. **Goldenrod** (or Solidago)
This sub-species of the lowlands becomes, in the mountains, a sub-species (or variety) with slightly larger capitula and straight, or short-branched, stems.

52. **Colt's-foot** (or Foalswort, Coughweed)
An easy herb to recognize: its early flowering long precedes the leaves. At the vegetative stage, however, it is possible to confuse the leaves of the colt's-foot with those of the butterbur (*Petasites hybridus* (L.) Gaertn.); one of the differences between the two is found on the upper side of the basal leaves, which carry short hairs in the case of the butterbur and long ones in the case of the colt's-foot.

53. **Tansy**
Syn: Chrysanthemum vulgare (L.) Bernh.
Herb with a very distinctive smell when crushed.

54. **Cotton lavender**
Often cultivated in borders because of its velvety touch and strong perfume, as well as its ability to withstand pruning, like box; unfortunately it hates frosts.

55. **Dandelion**
Taraxacum vulgare Shrank is a collective species uniting several sub-species which are very difficult to distinguish.

56. **Blessed thistle** (Holy thistle)
This yellow-flowered plant does not belong to the genus *Carduus*; its properties are similar to those of the milk thistle (*Silybum marianum* (L.) Gaertn.).

57. **Mouse-ear hawkweed**
Its diuretic properties have been rather eclipsed by those of a new arrival from Northern America, the Canadian fleabane (pl 72), which has become widespread.

58. **Ribbed melilot**
The white melilot (*Melilotus alba* Med.) has properties which enable it to substitute for the ribbed melilot; this is also the case with the golden melilot (*Melilotus altissima* Thuill.), the flowers of which are yellow like those of the ribbed one, but whose pod is hairy.

59. **Agrimony** (or Cocklebur)
The scented agrimony (*Agrimonia repens* L.) does not possess the same qualities as the common agrimony; they are very similar, but the former can be distinguished by the presence of numerous glands on the underside of the leaves.

60. **Herb bennet**
The leaves with three folioles (at least those on the stem) and the fruits (achenes with long hooked tips) are clearly visible in the photograph.

61. **Large yellow gentian**
This gentian cannot be mistaken for any other; it can however be taken for a member of the *Liliaceae*, the false helleborine (*Veratrum album* L.), which grows in the same habitat but has alternate leaves.

62. **Great mullein** (Aaron's rod)
Two other species, *Verbascum densiflorum* Bertol. and *Verbascum phlomoides* L., do not possess the same qualities (or not in the same degree) as the common mullein. These species can easily be mistaken; the great mullein can be distinguished by its smaller flowers (maximum diameter 25mm (1in), as opposed to the 30–40mm (1⅛–c1½in) of the other two species).

63. **Meadowsweet**
Syn: Spiraea ulmaria L.
One of our best medicinal herbs, impossible to confuse with others.

64. **Bay**
One should avoid confusing this with the oleander (*Nerium oleander* L.), which is toxic, or with the cherry laurel (*Prunus laurocerasus* L.), also toxic. The leaves of the latter are quite different, bigger, not aromatic and of a brighter green.

65. **Alder buckthorn**
Syn: Rhamnus frangula L.
See also under pl 24. Its fruits are toxic.

66. **Spindle**
A bush easy to identify thanks to its young branches of a dirty green

and four-cornered in section and to its fruits (red berries) which look a little like a priest's cap.

67. White bryony
Syn: Bryonia dioica Jacq.

68. Elder
The grape elder, or red-berried elder (*Sambucus racemosa* L.) has red fruits and prefers higher altitudes. The dwarf elder, or danewort (*S. ebulus* L.) has black fruits, like this elder; it is equally medicinal but is an herbaceous plant rather than a woody shrub.

69. Masterwort
Its habitat spreads to the European mountains between 1400 and 2700m (*c* 4500–9000ft). Lower down (but still above 400m/*c* 1500ft) it has naturalized, spread by ancient cultivation.

70. Hogweed (or Cow parsnip)
The most common of the *Umbelliferae* with white flowers, at least outside the Mediterranean basin; the hardiest as well, and the easiest to recognize.

71. Wild carrot
The cultivated carrot is a sub-species whose underground organs have become tubers (*ssp. sativus* (Hoffm.) Arcang.)

72. Canadian fleabane
Syn: Erigeron canadensis L.

73. Knotgrass
A herb assuming various forms; its creeping stems can be up to 1m (*c* 3ft) long; its flowers are either solitary or, more often, borne in small clusters at the base of the leaves.

74. White horehound
The inflorescences, of the simple cyme type, are grouped by the base of the leaves, as is often the case with the *Labiatae*. The flowers can also form dense verticils.

75. White dead-nettle
Its vague similarity to the nettle (pl 8) has given it its vernacular name. The plant however is not a stinging one and is no relative of the common nettle.

76. Hawthorn (or May, Whitethorn)
Among the most widespread species of hawthorn, this one has a single style; another has two (*Crataegus laevigata* (Poiret) DC.) and is endowed with the same medicinal properties.

77. Sloe (or Blackthorn)
This highly thorny bush can easily be distinguished from the other species of the genus *Prunus*.

78. Wild strawberry
Cultivated species have nothing in common with the European wild varieties; they are generally produced by crossing two American

species. The wild strawberry can be mistaken for a white-flowered barren strawberry (*Potentilla sterilis* (L.) Garcke) but it differs from the latter in its more acute foliar indentations and its touching or even superimposed petals.

79. Bramble
The collective species *Rubus fruticosus* L. covers more than a thousand sub-species, most of them very difficult to distinguish.

80. Gum cistus
Of all the white-flowered cistuses, the sunrose is the only one with large (5–10cm/1.9–3.9in) solitary flowers.

81. Great bindweed
Syn: Convolvulus sepium L.

82. Ramsons
Its leaves look more like those of the lily-of-the-valley than those of the cultivated garlic and disappear completely before the end of summer.

83. Guelder rose
A horticultural variety (cultivar *Roseum*) has only sterile flowers very similar to the peripheral flowers of the inflorescence of the guelder rose; this is the 'snow ball' of parks and gardens.

84. Woodruff
Syn: Asperula odorata L.
The smell of coumarin is released by drying.

85. Daisy
Other varieties with double flowers and various colours are in cultivation and can be found escaped from gardens.

86. Wild camomile
Syn: Matricaria recutita L.
This species can be confused with the widespread and very similar scentless mayweed (*Matricaria perforata* Merat); it differs in its strong smell of camomile. As for the feverfew (pl 87), the distinction is easier. Camomile (*Anthemis nobilis* L.), the best officinal herb, is part of a different genus to which also belong several species often mistaken for the wild camomile.

87. Feverfew
Syn: Chrysanthemum parthenium (L.) Bernh.

88. Shepherd's-purse
A highly variable species but easy to distinguish.

89. Garlic mustard (or Hedge garlic, Jack-by-the-Hedge)
Syn: Alliaria officinalis Andrz.
It emits a strong smell of garlic when crushed.

90. Watercress
The small-leaved cress is easily mistaken for watercress, but its good qualities are found in the fruits and seed-pods. It is cultivated for the same reasons as the various varieties of watercress.

91. Winter savory
Summer savory (*Satureia hortensis* L.) is an annual plant with the same properties and the same geographical origin.

92. Dog-rose (or Briar, Eglantine)
This is the most widespread and robust of all eglantines; they all possess the same qualities.

93. Wild angelica
Wild angelica has the same properties, albeit milder, as garden angelica (*Angelica archangelica* L.). The latter is indigenous to Scandinavia and Central and Eastern Europe; in other areas, it grows sporadically, usually escaped from cultivation.

94. Yarrow (or Milfoil)

95. Bogbean
It belongs to a family close to the *Gentianaceae*, with which it shares numerous properties.

96. Cowberry
Cowberry has distinctive red fruits; it belongs to the same botanical genus as the bilberry (pl 118) which is, however, deciduous while the cowberry is an evergreen.

97. Wood sorrel (or Wild shamrock)

98. Garden thyme
While normally its flowers are hermaphrodite, some are only female. Garden thyme is not the only one in cultivation; wild thyme (pl 109) and the hybrid form lemon thyme (*Thymus* × *citriodorus* (Pers.) Schreb.) are also grown. The hybrid is a culinary herb.

99. Valerian (or Garden heliotrope)
Syn: Valeriana officinalis auct. non L.

100. Soapwort (or Bouncing bet, Fuller's herb)
Native of the Mediterranean basin, soapwort has become naturalized in the north due to cultivation. One can often find also the cultivar with double leaves.

101. Hemp agrimony (or Boneset, Gravelroot)

102. Marsh mallow (or Mallards)
Many people confuse the marsh mallow with the hollyhock (*Althaea rosea* L. Cav.), which belongs to the same genus and is in cultivation, or even with the common mallow (pl 114), the properties of which are very similar.

103. Black horehound
The horehound is divided into six sub-species. The photograph shows the *ssp. foetida* Hayek: the boundaries of its habitat, particularly in the north, are still little known.

104. Motherwort
Although the map shows its habitat as covering the whole of Europe

except for the Mediterranean basin, this is an uncommon plant growing mainly near houses.

105. **Marjoram** (or Oregano)
As well as symmetrically bilateral flowers typical of the *Labiatae*, marjoram sometimes bears female flowers of radial symmetry.

It is sometimes mistaken for cultivated marjoram (*Origanum marjorana* L.), native of Northern Africa and grown in Europe.

106. **Wild basil**
It is difficult to confuse this herb, even at the vegetative stage, with germander speedwell (pl 139), the leaves of which have the same design.

107. **Clary** (or Cleareye)
An unmistakable herb, growing along lanes and widely cultivated for its musk-like perfume. Its white flowers, tinged with blue and with lilac-pink bracts, are arranged on small verticillated cymes.

108. **Meadow clary**
This mildly aromatic herb bears both hermaphrodite and female-only flowers.

109. **Wild thyme** (or Mother of thyme)
Wild thyme is the most widespread of the genus; the stem is angular with hairs on the corners. The northern boundary of its habitat is still little known. The other species, particularly the narrow-leaved thyme (*Thymus serpyllum* L.), have less angular stems.

110. **Herb Robert**
This geranium has nothing in common with the geraniums known in horticulture, which belong to the genus *Pelargonium*.

111. **Bistort** (or Snake-weed)

112. **Common centaury**
Syn: Centaurium umbellatum auct.

113. **Fumitory**
Often classified within a separate family, the *Fumariaceae*, this herb is linked by *Flora Europaea* with the *Papaveraceae* (sub-family of the *Fumarioideae*).

114. **Common mallow**
It can be distinguished from the other mallows – which have the same properties – by the deep notches in the petals, which are 15–20 mm (⁵/₈–¹³/₁₆ in) long, and by the shallow indentations on the leaves (less than 2–3mm (*c* ¹/₈ in)). One of the cultivars is widely grown.

115. **Foxglove**
Not to be gathered by amateurs.

116. **Salad burnet** (or Burnet bloodwort)
Syn: Poterium sanguisorba L.
The petal-less flowers are sometimes hermaphrodite, sometimes only female, sometimes only male.

117. **Ling** (or Common heather)
It is difficult to confuse this with the heaths of the genus *Erica*.

118. **Bilberry** (or Whortleberry)
Its blackish-blue fruits cannot be mistaken for those of the cowberry (pl 96).

119. **Chives**
Native of the mountains of Central Europe, this herb has become naturalized in several areas where it sometimes grows sub-spontaneously.

120. **Red valerian**
A similar species with narrow leaves of about 2 mm/⅛ in (*Centranthus angustifolius* (Mill.) DC.) grows at altitudes of up to 2000 m/*c* 6000 ft. The red valerian bears pink, red, white and even purple flowers.

121. **Lesser burdock**
This species is sometimes divided into a number of sub-species. Here it is treated as one.

122. **Purple loosestrife**
Only the upper leaves are alternate, the lower ones being opposed or verticillate.

123. **Alpenrose**
The species illustrated has, on the underside of the leaves, rust-coloured scales; these are not present in a similar species, the hairy alpenrose (*Rhododendron hirsutum* L.), which is chalk-loving while the other grows on non-calcareous substratum.

124. **Common poppy**
Among the most widespread species of the genus *Papaver*, one should also know the long-headed poppy (*Papaver dubium* L.) and the prickly-headed (or pale) poppy (*Papaver argemone* L.). These two have fruits which are elongated and gradually contract towards the base; the corn poppy has fruits of equal width and length, rounded at the base.

125. **Turpentine tree**
The genus *Pistacia* includes, apart from the species in the illustration, another dozen species, notably the pistacio-tree (*Pistacia vera* L.), native of Asia and cultivated in the Mediterranean countries.

126. **Vervain**
The vervain (*Lippia citriodora* L.) is a bush belonging to the same family; it is a native of the American continent and cultivated in Europe.

127. **Round-leaved mint** (or Apple mint)
Syn: Mentha rotundifolia auct.
The classification of the mints is very complex. This one belongs to the group of mints with a spike arrangement, like many cultivated mints.

128. **Water mint**
This herb belongs to the group of mints bearing flowers in tiered

groups. The majority of cultivated mints are hybrids; one of the parents of peppermint (*Mentha* × *piperita* L.) is the water mint.

129. **Wild teasel**
Syn: Dipsacus sylvestris Huds.
The *Diupsacus sativus* (L.) Honck., once cultivated and of uncertain origin, is the real teasel and the one used to card wool.

130. **Rosemary**
The essence of rosemary, like that of several *Labiatae*, is toxic to the extent that internal consumption of the herb should never be excessive.

131. **Liquorice**
The liquorice wood is in fact the peeled rhizome.

132. **Lady's-smock** (or Cuckooflower)
Once cultivated as a pot-plant.

133. **Rough comfrey**
The common comfrey (*Symphytum officinale* L.) is very similar but its stems are leafed and its flowers, although of various colours (white, cream, purple, lilac) are never blue. The properties mentioned apply above all to this species. The rough comfrey was once cultivated for fodder.

134. **Perennial cornflower**
Often cultivated for ornamental purposes; one can frequently find it growing sub-spontaneously in the plains.

135. **Wild pansy** (or Heartsease)
The photograph shows the *ssp. subalpina* Gaudin.

136. **Bittersweet** (or Woody nightshade)
The red fruits are considered to be toxic.

137. **Borage**
Native of Northern Africa; in the Western Mediterranean it is more or less naturalized, although its northern boundaries cannot be accurately traced. The map should be read with this in mind.

137. **Lesser periwinkle**
One can find sub-spontaneous cultivated forms.

139. **Germander speedwell**
See notes on pl 106.

140. **Chicory**
The lettuces and endives of kitchen gardens descend from chicory, which is considerably more potent. Its geographical distribution is difficult to assess precisely, particularly to the north of the area into which it has been introduced and naturalized.

141. **Ground ivy**
This herb has nothing to do with real ivy, a robust climber.

142. **Lavender**
Syn: Lavandula vera DC.

Other lavenders have more or less the same properties, particularly the broad-leaved lavender (*Lavandula latifolia* DC). In cultivation, the hardy hybrids derived from the two species discussed here are widely used.

143. **Sage**

The colour of the flowers varies from white to mauve, through blue and pink. The aromatic oil is as toxic as the one extracted from wormwood (pl 27).

144. **Hyssop**

A herb of variable form, often divided into sub-species or varieties: little is known about their individuality and classification.

APPENDIX II

Herbs and health

Any first approach to herbal medicine – ie treatment based on plants – should be as straightforward and as rigorous as possible. This chapter is meant only to suggest some basic treatments which will allow the beginner to deal with ordinary afflictions, as well as to supplement allopathic medications with a complementary cure. In fact, herbal treatment can do a lot more than this, but it then becomes the province of a specialist since the basic problem is, and always will be, that of an exact diagnosis, an essential first step towards all serious medication. We all think we know the state of our health, but sometimes there is no worse judge than oneself. And as for coming to conclusions and giving advice on someone else's health . . .

Each therapy has its limitations and this applies also to herbalism: it would be ridiculous to try to treat a serious case of pneumonia uniquely with herbs; on the other hand, their field of action – wider than one thinks – should not be underestimated. A common-sense rule is not to ask everything of them, neither of chemiotherapy nor of homoeopathy, but to keep each in its proper place according to its merits.

The properties of the herbs can only have effect as long as well-proven methods of application are respected. The ways of preparing them are precisely worked out in order, on the one hand, to extract the active substances without neutralizing them, and on the other to administer them to the organism in the form best suited to achieve the required effect.

We give below, first, some basic information connected with the preparation and use of the extracts; then, a glossary of the therapeutic properties combining a definition of the most commonly-used terms with the name of the herbs endowed with those particular properties; and finally a short list of ailments which can be treated or alleviated by the herbs.

1. HOW TO PREPARE AND USE THE PLANTS

The herbs are used either fresh or at the end of more or less extended preservation. They are used fresh when their active principles run the risk of fading or altering in the course of preservation. Whether fresh or dried, the extracts must be subjected to a certain amount of preparation before being administered.

A. The preparation

The procedures briefly described below are the simplest and do not cover the galenic preparations – such as extracts, intracts, hydrolates, alcoholates – which should be produced by qualified and well-equipped experts.

One should not use vessels with exposed metal parts, particularly iron utensils (which are now quite rare). Any other material will do; enamel, earthenware or porcelain, thick wood or glass.

a) *Fresh juice*

Fresh plants are finely cut, chopped, pounded and finally pressed either through thick linen or with a small press. The juice is then filtered or taken as it is.

b) *Powders*

Dried extracts can be used as they are, after having been powdered. This should be carried out shortly before the application.

c) *Brews*

Dried herbs, roughly pounded, are mixed with a cold liquid, which could be oil, wine or water. The infusion time varies according to the plant from a few hours to a whole night. These preparations cannot be made to last.

Tinctures are macerations carried out in alcohol at 70°C (140°F), sometimes for two to ten days.

d) *Decoctions*

The cold water in which the dried herbs are steeped is slowly brought to boil; the mixture must boil under cover for 10 to 30 minutes according to the plant. This method is the one more often used for hard organs, such as bark.

e) *Infusions*

Boiling water is poured onto the plant or, more often, the plant is thrown into the boiling water, left for a quick boil, covered and allowed to stew for a period ranging from a few minutes to a quarter of an hour.

B. The usage

a) *Ingestion*

The most common way to administer the drug, be it fresh juice, a brew, an infusion or a decoction. Powders can be mixed with foodstuffs.

b) *Fumigation and inhalation*

One can make the most of the beneficial properties of aromatic fumes and vapours either by letting the herbs burn slowly on embers or by boiling them in water.

c) *Internal use (without ingestion)*

The active principles extracted through maceration, infusion or decoction, as well as chopped up fresh plants, can be used other than by ingestion. They could be used to irrigate natural cavities (mouth, ears, vagina, anus) by gargle, injection or enema.

d) *External use*

The preparations can also be used as lotions (a light wash with a soaked gauze), as complete or partial baths (foot baths, hip-baths), as pledgets (soaked gauze applied for a certain time on the affected part) or as cataplasms (poultice of fresh pounded herbs or preparations of dried herbs softened by decoction and wrapped in a piece of linen).

2. GLOSSARY OF THERAPEUTIC PROPERTIES

This glossary gives a definition of the properties attributed to the plants and lists, as examples, the main species endowed with such virtues. It also allows a quick comparison between plants with analogous properties. The figure after each herb refers to the plate number.

Abortive, terminates a pregnancy: Birthwort 28 / Rue 32 / Biting stonecrop 34 / Tansy 53 / White bryony 67.

Allopathy, classical medicine which follows the law of opposites in its treatment of ailments: therapy is based on achieving a result opposite to the symptom presented by the patient.

Analgesic, suppresses or attenuates pain sensitiveness: Cowslip 47 / Water mint 128.

Anaphrodisiac, attenuates sexual desires: Hops 25.

Anti-anaemic, treats anaemia, balances the blood composition, brings back strength: Common nettle 8 / Watercress 90 / Dog-rose 92.

Anti-arthritic, suited for the treatment of articular afflictions with inflammatory causes: Biting stonecrop 34 / Meadowsweet 63 / Bryony 67 / Alpenrose 123.

Anti-asthmatic, prevents asthmatic attacks: Colt's-foot 52 / Valerian 99.

Antibiotic, a substance, essentially excreted by a micro-organism, which prevents the development of, and selectively destroys, bacteria: Mouse-ear hawkweed 57 / Lesser burdock 121 / Purple loosestrife 122.

Anticatarrhal, treats the inflammations of the mucous membranes of the respiratory ducts: Elecampane 44 / Cowslip 47 / Colt's-foot 52.

Anticonvulsive, prevents convulsions (involuntary spasms of muscles and limbs): Valerian 99 / Red valerian 120.

Antidiabetic, see Hypoglycemic.

Antidiarrhoeic, stops diarrhoea and controls intestinal movements: Ribwort plantain 5 / Common nettle 8 / genus *Potentilla* 35, 36, 37 / Herb bennet 60 / Wild carrot 71 / Canadian fleabane 72 / Knotgrass 73 / Wild strawberry 78 / Bramble 79 / Bistort 111 / Ling 117 / Bilberry 118 / Purple loosestrife 122.

Anti-ecchymotic, dissipates ecchymoses and soothes the pain they cause: Arnica 43 / White bryony 67 / Masterwort 69 / Common centaury 112 / Vervain 126 / Lesser periwinkle 138 / Lavender 142.

Antiemetic, used to suppress nausea: Wormwood 27.

Antihaemorrhagic, see Haemostatic.

Antihaemorrhoidal, cures haemorrhoids, varicose sores formed around the anus and in the rectum by the dilation of the veins: Water-pepper 3 / Lesser celandine 38 / Herb bennet 60 / Yarrow 94 / Bistort 111 / Bittersweet 136.

Anti-inflammatory, treats the inflammation related to infections, or to rheumatism: Ribwort plantain 5 / Couch grass 16 / Tormentil 35 / Great mullein 62 / Wild camomile 86 / Marsh mallow 102 / Common mallow 114 / Liquorice 131 / Perennial cornflower 134.

Antilactiferous, stops the secretion of milk: Alder 20 / Lesser periwinkle 138.

Antilithiasic, prevents the formation of, or dissolves, the calculi in the excretion ducts of the glands (urinary, biliary, salivary ducts): Wild strawberry 78 / Alpenrose 123.

Antimitotic, inhibits cellular division and prevents the uncontrolled proliferation of cancerous cells: Greater celandine 40 / Common ragwort 50.

Antineuralgic, treats neuralgias, aches and pains of the nerves: Elder 68 / Alpenrose 123 / Vervain 126.

Antiplethoric, reduces the excess of blood in the organism: Fumitory 113 / Bittersweet 136.

Antipruriginous, relieves the itching caused by skin afflictions or insect bites: Ribwort plantain 5 / Common lady's-mantle 31 / Elecampane 44 / Wild carrot 71 / White horehound 74 / Purple loosestrife 122.

Antirheumatic, relieves rheumatic pain and helps to treat the cause: Sweet vernal grass 7 / Scots pine 15 / Broom 46 / Ribbed melilot 58 / Meadowsweet 63 / Bay 64 / Canadian fleabane 72 / Lesser burdock 121 / Bittersweet 136 / Borage 137.

Antiscorbutic, prevents or treats scurvy, an illness caused by the lack or insufficient quantity of vitamin C in the diet (fever, anaemia, haemorrhages, gastro-enteritis): Common sorrel 2 / Glasswort 18 / Hawthorn 76 / Bramble 79 / Garlic mustard 89 / Watercress 90 / Dog-rose 92 / Bogbean 95 / Fumitory 113 / Chives 119 / Lady's-smock 132.

186

Antiseptic, prevents or treats infection by destroying microbes or by impeding their development: Juniper 14 / Tormentil 35 / Perforate St John's-wort 49 / Bay 64 / Winter savory 91 / Thyme 98 / Ling 117 / Chives 119 / Lavender 142.

Antispasmodic, relieves spasms and muscular cramps (muscles of the hollow organs: stomach, intestines, uterus, etc), convulsions and similar nervous afflictions: Lady's bedstraw 29 / Common lady's-mantle 31 / Greater celandine 40 / Ribbed melilot 58 / Hawthorn 76 / Gum cistus 80 / Wild camomile 86 / Feverfew 87 / Valerian 99 / Marjoram 105 / Wild thyme 109 / Liquorice 131.

Antisudorific, cuts down on perspiration: Clary 107 / Meadow sage 108 / Sage 143.

Antithrombotic, prevents the formation of clots in the bloodstream: Common melilot 58.

Antitumoral, see Antimitotic.

Antitussive, tending or having the power to control or prevent coughing: Verbascum 62.

Aperitive, (bitter aperitive), stimulates the appetite: Wormwood 27 / Blessed thistle 56 / Large yellow gentian 61 / Common centaury 112 / Chicory 140.

Aphrodisiac, increases or resurrects sexual desires: Hogweed 70 / Winter savory 91.

Aromatherapy, treatment of illnesses with the help of vegetal essences.

Astringent, contracts tissues and mucous membranes, can control secretions and stop pathological glows, as well as hasten the cicatrizing of wounds: Sessile oak 21 / Lady's bedstraw 29 / Common lady's-mantle 31 / genus *Potentilla* 35, 36, 37 / Agrimony 59 / Wild strawberry 78 / Purple loosestrife 122.

Bacteriostatic, a substance which stops the proliferation of bacteria without killing them: Hops 25.

Balsamic, acts on the respiratory ducts by stimulating them and soothing the mucous membranes: Scots pine 15 / Thyme 98.

Bechic, a remedy for coughs: Common polypody 9 / Hart's-tongue 10 / Marjoram 105 / Germander speedwell 139 / Ground ivy 141 / Hyssop 144.

Biocatalyst (or Biocatalytic), the presence of this substance accelerates vital functions: fermentations, hormones, vitamins, trace elements: Sea buckthorn 17 / Wild carrot 71 / Sloe 77 / Ramsons 82.

Bitter-tonic, see Aperitive.

Carcinogenic, capable of producing the formation of a malignant tumour: Common ragwort 50.

Cardiotonic, tones the heart and regulates its rhythm: Wallflower 42 / Broom 46 / White horehound 74 / Hawthorn 76.

Carminative, helps to expel intestinal gases (a remedy against aerophagy and swelling of the abdomen): Yellow flag 41 / Masterwort 69 / Winter savory 91 / Wild angelica 93 / Wild thyme 109 / Salad burnet 116.

Chlorurolytic, diuretic which eliminates the chlorides produced by oedemas: Downy birch 19 / Borage 137.

Cholagogue, facilitates the flow of bile: Mugwort 6 / Hart's-tongue 10 / Dandelion 55 / Mouse-ear hawkweed 57 / Alder buckthorn 65 / Woodruff 84 / Mints 127, 128.

Chloretic, increases the flow of bile: Downy birch 19 / Large-leaved lime 33 / Dandelion 55 / Black horehound 103 / Lesser burdock 121.

Cicatrizing, helps the cicatrization of wounds: genus *Potentilla* 35, 36, 37 / Kidney vetch 45 / Clary 107 / Germander speedwell 139.

Convulsive, provokes violent and involuntary contractions of the muscles (convulsions): Hyssop 144.

Decongestant, facilitates the flow of an organic liquid which has accumulated somewhere in the body: Agrimony 59 (stomach, liver, gall-bladder).

Depurative, purifies the organism by encouraging the elimination of toxins and poisons: Pellitory-of-the-wall 4 / Common nettle 8 / Couchgrass 16 / Glasswort 18 / Wild strawberry 78 / Ramsons 82 / Daisy 85 / Soapwort 100 / Wild teasel 129.

Detergent, cleans and treats wounds and ulcers: Blessed thistle 56 / Black horehound 103.

Digestive, facilitates the digestion: Wormwood 27 / Fennel 30 / Tansy 53 / Blessed thistle 56 / Woodruff 84 / Round-leaved mint 127 / Perennial cornflower 134.

Disinfectant, see Antiseptic.

Diuretic, increases urinary secretions: several species have diuretic properties, among them: Horsetail 12 / Sea buckthorn 17 / Dandelion 55 / Meadowsweet 63 / Garlic mustard 89 / Cowberry 96 / Ling 117.

Drastic, strong purgative: Birthwort 28 / Alder buckthorn 65 / White bryony 67.

Emetic, provokes vomiting: Yellow flag 41 / Alder buckthorn 65 / Spindle 66 / White bryony 67.

Emmenagogue, regulates the menses and attenuates or relieves the troubles connected with them: Wormwood 27 / Rue 32 / Common ragwort 50 / Tansy 53 / Feverfew 87 / Yarrow 94 / Bogbean 95 / Motherwort 104 / Clary 107 / Sage 143.

Emollient, has a soothing, relaxing effect on inflamed tissues (external and/or internal use): Great mullein 62 / Masterwort 69 / Marsh mallow 102 / Common mallow 114 / Common poppy 124 / Liquorice 131 / Comfrey 133 / Borage 137.

Expectorant, facilitates the expulsion of excessive bronchial secretion: Common polypody 9 / Cowslip 47 / Colt's-foot 52 / White horehound 74 / Daisy 85 / Liquorice 131 / Wild pansy 135 / Hyssop 144.

Febrifuge, reduces fever, can prevent the repetition of periodical feverish attacks: Downy birch 19 / Alder 20 / Ash 22 / Meadowsweet 63 / Elder 68 / Feverfew 87 / Common centaury 112.

Fungicide, destroys parasitic funguses: Winter savory 91.

Galactagogue, increases milk secretion: Fennel 30 / Wild carrot 71.

Haemolytic, destroys red corpuscles: Yellow flag 41.

Haemostatic, coagulant and constrictor of the blood vessels used to stop haemorrhages: Water-pepper 3 / Ribwort plantain 5 / Horsetail 12 / Wild carrot 71 / White dead-nettle 75 / Shepherd's-purse 88.

Homoeopathy, contrary to allopathy, it relies on the law of similarities: the remedy administered in minimal doses would produce, in a healthy subject, symptoms similar to those of the illness to be treated.

Hypertensive, raises the blood pressure: Broom 46 / Fumitory 113.

Hypoglycemic, remedy against diabetes: it lowers the sugar level in the blood: Common nettle 8 / Bilberry 118 / Lesser periwinkle 138 / Chicory 140 / Sage 143.

Hypotensive, lowers the blood pressure: Stonecrop 34 / Arnica 43 / Hogweed 70 / Hawthorn 76 / Ramsons 82 / Black horehound 130 / Lesser periwinkle 138.

Insecticide, kills insects: Wormwood 27 / Feverfew 87 / Lavender 142.

Laxative, mild purgative: Ribwort plantain 5 / Common polypody 9 / Charlock 48 / Alder buckthorn 65 / Elder 68 / Sloe 77 / Dog-rose 92 / Hemp agrimony 101 / Common mallow 114.

Metrorrhagia, uterine haemorrhage taking place outside the menses. The following species can cure it: Horsetail 12 / White dead-nettle 75 / Shepherd's purse 88.

Narcotic, brings on sleep and relieves pain: Hops 25 / Woodruff 84 / Common poppy 124.

Oestrogene, strengthens the female sexual characteristics: Hops 25 / Sage 143.

Ophthalmic, can be used as a treatment for the eyes: Ribbed melilot 58 / Wild camomile 86 / Herb Robert 110.

Parasiticide, kills parasites: Bay 64 / Spindle 66 / Prickly juniper 13 (veterinary use).

Pectoral, used to treat the afflictions of the respiratory ducts: Great mullein 62 / Elder 68 / Common poppy 124 / Liquorice 131 / Borage 137.

Phytotherapy, the treatment of illnesses with fresh or dried plants or with natural extracts.

Purgative, a strong stimulant of intestinal evacuations (dangerous!): Monk's rhubarb 1 / Ash 22 / Dog's mercury 23 / Common buckthorn 24 / Alder buckthorn 65 / White bryony 67 / Great bindweed 81.

Refreshing, moderates the body temperature and is endowed with laxative properties (refreshing tisane): Couchgrass 16 / Wood sorrel 97 / Round-leaved mint 127 / Liquorice 131 / Wild chicory 140.

Remineralizing, re-establishes the mineral equilibrium in the body by introducing mineral salts and rare elements: Horsetail 12 / Glasswort 18 / Knotgrass 73 / Wild strawberry 78.

Resolutive, a remedy which relieves and dispels obstructions, oedemas, swellings: Colt's-foot 52 / Watercress 90.

Revulsive, provokes a superficial afflux of blood (external use) in order to relieve an organ affected by congestion or inflammation: Arnica 43 / Tansy 53 / White bryony 67 / Elder 68 / Chives 119.

Rubefacient, when applied on the skin provokes reddening and the impression of heat: Juniper 14 / Rue 32 / Yellow flag 41 / Arnica 43 / Charlock 48 / Elder 68 / Ramsons 82.

Sedative, lowers the hyperactivity of the nervous system and calms irritation: Sweet vernal grass 7 / Lady's bedstraw 29 / Large-leaved lime 33 / Common ragwort 50 / Hawthorn 76 / Marsh mallow 102 / Black horehound 103.

Somniferous, see Narcotic; also: Lime 33 / Ribbed melilot 58 / Valerian 99.

Soothing, see Emollient.

Spasmolytic, see Antispasmodic.

Stimulant, excites fairly rapidly, albeit with short-lived effect, the organic and/or psychic functions: Winter savory 91 / Hemp agrimony 101.

Stomachic, stimulates the stomach and improves the digestion: Silverweed 36 / Elecampane 44 / Blessed thistle 56 / Herb bennet 60 / Hogweed 70 / Wild camomile 86 / Wild angelica 93 / Thyme 98 / Clary 107 / Wild thyme 109.

Sudorific, increases perspiration: Downy birch 19 / Elder 68 / Common poppy 124 / Wild pansy 135 / Borage 137 / Lavender 142.

Tonic, permanently reconstitutes or develops the energy potential of certain organs or of the organism as a whole: Mugwort 6 / Sea buckthorn 17 / Alder 20 / Samphire 26 / Common lady's-mantle 31 / Watercress 90 / Winter savory 91 / Bogbean 95 / Round-leaved mint 127.

Topic, general term indicating drugs to be used externally.

Uricolytic, eliminates uric acid within the organism (gout, rheumatisms): Common nettle 8 / Juniper 14 / Ash 22 / Blessed thistle 56 / Mouse-ear hawkweed 57 / Meadowsweet 63.

Vasodilating, increases the diameter of the blood vessels and has therefore a favourable effect on hypertension (high blood pressure): Lesser periwinkle 138.

Vermifuge, destroys or expels intestinal worms: Common polypody 9 / Male fern 11 (against tape-worm) / Rock samphire 26 / Wormwood 27 (against ascarides) / Tansy 53 / Cotton lavender 54 / Ramsons 82 / Thyme 98.

Vomitory, see Emetic.
Vulnerary, see Cicatrizing.

3. ALPHABETICAL TABLE OF AILMENTS AND TREATMENTS

Herbal treatment

This table is certainly not comprehensive. Being part of a guide, it could hardly compete with a treatise. Like the rest of the book, it is meant as an introduction to the knowledge of remedial herbs: faced with the considerable number of phytotherapeutic formulae in existence, it limits itself to a few basic suggestions.

The formulae given here as examples will prove effective with certain individuals rather than with others. The empiricism which is behind each discovery of an effective remedy is never so obvious as in chemotherapy; it is therefore always advisable to experiment with the most appropriate formula for each temperament.

The application of a herbal medication requires, like all the rest, a strict hygienic routine.

The doses below are suited to adults of around 70 kg (c 11 st); they should be halved in the case of teenagers and cut down to a quarter for children. Unless otherwise stated, the quantities are based on net weights in grammes per litre of water. The dosage is usually expressed by the number of cups per day.

Illness	Herb and organs	Quantity (g/l of water)	Type and time of preparation	Posology (cups per day)
Acne	Sloe 77 flowers	50	Infusion 10 min	× 2
	Soapwort 100 roots	100	Decoction 10 min	lotion
Albuminuria	Broom 46 flowers	30	Infusion 10 min	× 3 for 10 days
Angina	Daisy 85 leaves and flowers	60	Infusion 10 min	× 3 between meals
	Bistort 111 rhizome	60	Infusion 10 min filtered and sugared	gargle
Aphta	see **Stomatitis**			
Arterio-sclerosis	Lady's-mantle 31 leaves	40	Decoction	× 3 between meals
Arthritis	see **Gout**			
Asthenia (physical)	Sea buckthorn 17 fruits		Jellies	
	Dog-rose 92 fruits			
	Winter savory 91 whole plant	30	Infusion 10 min	× 2
Asthma	Common mallow 114 flowers and leaves	50	Boiled	inhalation
Blepharitis	Ribbed melilot 58 flowering tips	100	Infusion to be used immediately	lotion several times a day
Bronchitis	Cowslip 47 flowers	30	Infusion 10 min	× 3
Burns	Comfrey 133 raw rhizome			cataplasm
	Great mullein 62 flowers			pledgets
Cardio-vascular afflictions	Hawthorn 76 flowers	15	Infusion 10 min	× 2 for 20 days
Caries (dental)	Garlic mustard 89 fresh leaves			chew
Cellulitis	Couchgrass 16 fresh rhizome		Juice	4 soupspoons a day

Illness	Herb and organs	Quantity (g/l of water)	Type and time of preparation	Posology (cups per day)
Chilblains	Great mullein 62 fresh leaves and flowers	60 per litre of milk	Decoction 10 min	lotion once in the evening
Cholesterol	Downy birch 19 bark	10	Decoction + infusion 5 min each	11 a day
	Ash 22 leaves	10		
Colds	Ground ivy 141 flowered plant	15	Infusion 10 min	× 2–3
Conjunctivitis	Liquorice 131 roots	100	Infusion 60 min	pledgets
Constipation	Hemp agrimony 101 roots	30	Decoction 2 min + infusion 15 min	2 × day before meals
Contusion (without wound)	Agrimony 59 leaves	100	Filtered decoction 15 min	pledgets
Coughs 1. Soothing	Marjoram 105 flowering tips	10	Infusion 10 min	× 2–3 between meals
2. Expectorant	White horehound 74 flowering tips and leaves	15–30	Infusion 15 min	× 3 before meals
Cramps (stomach)	see **Gastralgia**			
Demineral- ization	Horsetail 12 stems	50	Decoction 30 min	3 wine glasses a day before meals
Depression	Valerian 99 fresh roots	10 per glass of cold water	Maceration 1 night + sugar + flavouring	× 2 for 8 days
Diarrhoea	Knotgrass 73 whole plant	30	Infusion 10 min	× 2
Dyspepsia	Blessed thistle 56 flowering tips	40	Infusion 10 min	× 2 before meals
Ecchymosis	see **Contusion**			

Illness	Herb and organs	Quantity (g/l of water)	Type and time of preparation	Posology (cups per day)
Eczema	Wild teasel 129 roots	40	Decoction 10 min	× 2
Fever	Common centaury 112 flowering tips	20	Infusion 10 min	× 2
	Alder 20 bark	15 per 1 white wine	Maceration	6 soupspoons a day
Flatulence	Masterwort 69 rhizome	30	Infusion 10 min	3 × day after meals
Frigidity	Hogweed 70 roots and leaves	50	Infusion 10 min	× 1 (evening)
Gastralgia	Silverweed 36 leaves	30	Decoction 1–2 min + infusion 10 min	mid-way between meals
Gout	Canadian fleabane 72 plant	50	Decoction 2 min + infusion 10 min	× 1/2 a day
	Lesser burdock 121 fresh leaves	Cataplasm of crushed leaves on the joints		
Haemorrhoids	White dead-nettle 75 flowers and leaves	50	Infusion 10 min	× 2
	Yarrow 94 flowering tips and leaves	50	Decoction 10 min	soaked pledgets
Hepatic insufficiency	Common polypody 9 rhizome	40	Decoction 1 min + infusion 10 min	× 3
Hoarseness	Agrimony 59 leaves	100	Decoction 4 min	gargle × 3 a day
Hypertension	Lesser periwinkle 138 leaves	40	Decoction 3 min + infusion 5 min	× 3
Hypotension	Broom 46 branches	20	Infusion 10 min	2 soupspoons 5 × day for 8 days
Inappetence	Bogbean 95 fresh leaves	10 red wine	Infusion 10 min	2 soupspoons before meals
Indigestion	see Dyspepsia			
Insect bites	Elder 68 fresh leaves	rub the crushed leaves on the bite		
Insomnia	Woodruff 84 flowering tips	30	Infusion 10 min	1 cup at bedtime

Illness	Herb and organs	Quantity (g/l of water)	Type and time of preparation	Posology (cups per day)
Insufficient lactation	Fennel 30 seeds	30	Infusion 10 min	× 4 between meals
Itching	Wild carrot 71 root	40	Decoction 10 min	Lotion (several times a day)
Lithiasis (biliary)	Borage 137 aerial parts	40	Decoction 5 min + infusion 10 min	× 2
Lithiasis (kidneys)	Broom 46 flowers	25	Infusion 10 min	× 1 in two parts
Menses (painful or insufficient)	Wormwood 27 flowering tips	5	Infusion 5 min	× 2 (1 week before due)
Migraine	Water mint 128 leaves	20	Infusion 10 min	× 1
Palpitations	Motherwort 104 flowering tips	20	Infusion 10 min	× 1
Parasites (intestines): 1. Tape worm	Male fern 11 rhizome	15 g in a glass of water plus a purgative after four hours		
2. Pinworms	Cotton lavender 54 seed powder	2 g in some honey		
Rheumatism	Meadowsweet 63 flowers	50	Infusion 10 min	× 3 (for three weeks)
Sores	see Wounds			
Stomatitis	Bilberry 118 fruits	Retain the juice in the mouth while eating		
Tracheitis	Colt's-foot 52 flowers	50	Infusion 10 min	× 3
Warts	Greater celandine 40	Latex of fresh root mixed with glycerine		
Wounds (light)	Perforate St John's-wort 49 fresh flowering tips	500	Maceration in 1l of oil: 10 days in the sun	lotion
	Tormentil 35 rhizome	30	Decoction 10 min	lotion

APPENDIX III

Herbs in the kitchen

It is not our aim to suggest recipes, as there are so many books on the subject. Since the purpose of this guide is to draw attention to wild herbs and encourage their cultivation in kitchen gardens, we will just point out the potential of the world about us – not only the wild herbs with excellent culinary value but also those that provide us with unusual seasonings.

1. PRESERVES AND COMPOTES

The popularity of the cowberry (pl 96) and the bilberry (pl 118) should not make us forget other alternatives: the so-called 'fruits' of the sea buckthorn (pl 17) and of the dog-rose (pl 92), the blackberries (pl 79), the haws of the hawthorn (pl 76), the fruits of the guelder rose (pl 83, toxic when fresh) and of the elder (pl 68).

2. SALADS AND COOKED VEGETABLES

It is basically the young leaves that are used for springtime treatment: those of the dandelion (pl 55) and of the watercress (pl 90) are still often appreciated in salads, but the common nettle (pl 8), the cowslip (pl 47), the herb bennet (pl 60), the shepherd's-purse (pl 88), the lady's-smock (pl 132) and the wild chicory (pl 140) deserve to be brought back into the limelight.

The young shoots of the hop (pl 25) are still sometimes prepared like asparagus. The leaves of the silverweed (pl 36), the lesser celandine (pl 38), the dandelion (pl 55), the yarrow (pl 94) and the borage (pl 137) can be cooked just like spinach. The roots of the silverweed (pl 36) and the dandelion (pl 55), the rhizome of the herb bennet (pl 60) can be used as a substitute for salsifies.

3. SEASONINGS AND CONDIMENTS

We all know how to use chives (pl 119) in salads, but why not try the ribwort plantain (pl 5), the daisy (pl 85), the garlic mustard (pl 89), the wood sorrel (pl 97), in small quantities, like lemon, the salad burnet (pl 116) or the lady's-smock (pl 132)? By the same token, soups and vegetable stocks can benefit from the young leaves of the common sorrel (pl 2), the bistort (pl 111) or the ground ivy (pl 141), and potatoes can be garnished with ramsons (pl 82).

A great number of wild herbs can be used as condiments. Some species are well-known even if not widely appreciated: among them fennel (pl 30), bay (pl 64), thyme (pl 98), the large-leaved mint (pl 127), rosemary (pl 130), lavender (pl 142) and sage (pl 143). On the other hand, winter savory (pl 91), marjoram (pl 105), wild thyme (pl 109) and hyssop (pl 144) are only sparsely used these days. And how many still enjoy the young leaves of mugwort (pl 6), the dried and powdered fruits of the sea buckthorn (pl 17), the unripe cones of the hop (pl 25), or rue (pl 32), tansy (pl 53) and clary (pl 107)?

Finally, few are the gourmets who can still prepare, or know where to find, such delicious condiments, preserved in vinegar, as glasswort (pl 18), rock samphire (pl 26), the rhizomes of elecampane (pl 44), the flower buds of the broom (pl 46) or the young leaves of borage (pl 137).

4. WINES AND LIQUEURS

Woodruff (pl 84) is still used to flavour wines, but one cannot say the same of meadowsweet (pl 63) which could easily be used instead.

Liqueurs often owe their flavour to herbs, and some species are still used today by producers, such as the 'fruits' of the juniper (pl 14), the flowering tips of wormwood (pl 27), the fruits of fennel (pl 30), the roots of elecampane (pl 61) or of wild angelica (pl 93). Others are more appreciated by the amateur, who can ferment them at ease (sloes, pl 77).

GLOSSARY OF BOTANICAL TERMINOLOGY

The terms described in the chapter 'How to use this guide' are not repeated here.

Achene: small, dry one-seeded fruit.
Acicular: like a needle in shape.
Alburnum: sap-wood, a soft and generally pale kind of wood growing between the bark and the core of the tree.

Bipinnate: a leaf in which the folioles, disposed in pairs either side of the main nerve, are also indented and pinnate.
Bract: small leaf or scale situated at the base of the pedicil of a flower or of a peduncle.
Bulbil: small bulb capable of producing a new plant and growing at the base of a leaf or within an inflorescence.

Calcicole: a plant that grows solely or predominantly in alkaline medium rich in calcareous matter.
Chalice: external wrap of a flower, usually green, formed by separate or more or less welded parts.
Collar: the joint of stem and root.
Cone: the inflorescence of certain Gymnosperms (conifers) formed by scales · holding the ovules; it also designates any similar inflorescence.
Cordiform: heart-shaped.
Coumarin: a group of strongly-scented substances derived from organic acids present in a great variety of plants; *Graminaceae* and *Umbelliferae* are particularly endowed with them.
Cultivar: a cultivated strain selectively originated.

Diachaenium: or cremocarp, a double dry fruit breaking up into two one-seeded mericarps which hang from one peduncle forked at its extremity (*Umbelliferae*).

Flower stem: elongated axil ending in a flower or group of flowers and without leaves.
Foliole: one of the divisions of a compound leaf.

Indigenous: a plant growing and living spontaneously in a given area.
Inflorescence: a grouping of flowers around the same main axis; the

mode of development and arrangement of flowers on an axis.

Infructescence: the fruiting stage of an inflorescence.

Laciniate: cut into deep and narrow irregular segments.

Lanceolate: a narrow, long leaf tapering at each end.

Latex: a milky liquid which exudes from certain plants when the stem or the leaves are bruised.

Ligulate: strap-shaped; the flowers of the *Compositae* have a corolla consisting of a segment asymmetrically placed on one side only.

Naturalized: a plant indigenous in a foreign land but acclimatized, spreading and behaving like an indigenous species.

Nitrophyte: a plant requiring a soil rich in nitrogen; growing usually by farms, fields and sheepfolds.

Obovate: inversely ovate, the wider part being toward the top.

Palmate: a leaf in which the main nerves or the folioles radiate from the same point like the fingers of a hand.

Panicle: Inflorescence formed by a compound cluster, itself made of other clusters or of cymes.

Pedicil: small axil with a flower at the tip.

Petiole: slender part of a leaf linking the blade to the stem.

Phenology: branch of ecology concerned with the relationship between climatic phenomena and the growth and reproduction of plants.

Pinnate: a leaf in which the secondary nerves or the folioles are arranged in pairs either side of the main nerve like the barbs of a feather.

Pinnatifid: cleft in a pinnate manner; a pinnate leaf with the margin cut into deep lobes.

Pyrethrum: white-flowered composita, a relative of chrysanthemums, which, when dried, produces an insecticide powder.

Receptacle: axis of the flower, in the shape of a cone, a disc or a cup, onto which are rooted the floral involucres, the stamens, the ovary and the pistil(s).

Sagittate: shaped like an arrow-head.

Sessile: an organ sitting directly on the axis (leaf without petiole, flower without pedicil).

Spatulate: shaped like a spatula; a leaf wider at the top than at the base.

Spore: asexual reproductive cell which takes part in the propagation of the species, particularly in the case of mosses and ferns.

Stigma: swollen or feathery tip of a pistil: its surface, more or less viscous, holds the pollen.

Style: the elongated part of the pistil between the ovary and the stigma.

Synergy: reinforced action of two or more substances due to their combination; the effect of such association is stronger than the sum of the effects of the individual components.

Taxon: the name applied to a taxonomic group in a formal system of nomenclature: a species, a variety, a race.

Thallus: vegetative organ of leafless, stemless and rootless plants.

Tuberized: a stem or a root which has swollen to accumulate and reserve nutritional elements.

Tubulate: floral parts welded in the shape of an elongated tube.

Xerophilous: or xerophile, a plant living, or capable of living in dry areas (dry soil, dry climate).

FURTHER READING

Aichelle, D. and R. and Schwegler, H. and A., *Hamlyn Guide to Wild Flowers of Britain and Europe*, Hamlyn (1992)

Allen, D. E., *Flora of the Isle of Man*, Manx Museum (1986)

Baumann, Hellmut, *Greek Wild Flowers – and Plant Lore in Ancient Greece*, Herbert Press (1993)

Beckett, E., *Wildflowers of Majorca, Minorca and Ibiza*, Balkema (1988)

Bentley, G. and Trimen, H., *Medicinal Plants, Vols 1–4* (1991)

Bevis, *Flora of the Isle of Wight*, Isle of Wight NH Arch Soc

Blamey, Marjorie and Grey-Wilson, Christopher, *The Illustrated Flora of Britain and Northern Europe*, Hodder (1989)

Bonner, A., *Plants of the Balearic Islands* (1992)

Bremness, Lesley, *Complete Book of Herbs – A Practical Guide to Growing and Using Herbs*, Dorling Kindersley (1988)

Bunney, S., *Illustrated Encyclopedia of Herbs: Their Medicinal and Culinary Uses*, Chancellor (1993)

Chinery, *Field Guide to the Plant Life of Britain and Europe*, Kingfisher (1987)

Clapham, A. R., Tutin, T. G. and Moore, D. M., *Flora of the British Isles*, CUP (1989)

Clapham, A. R., Tutin, T. G. and Warburg, E. F., *Excursion Flora of the British Isles*, CUP (1981)

Cooper, Marion and Johnson, Anthony, *Poisonous Plants in Britain – and their Effects on Animals and Man*, HMSO (1984)

Council of Europe, *Vegetation of the Alps* (1983)

Crozier, J. and Matschke, A., *Flowers of Andorra*, ADN (1992)

Davies, Paul and Gibbons, Bob, *Field Guide to the Wild Flowers of Southern Europe*, Crowood (1993)

Ellis, G., *Flowering Plants of Wales*, National Museum of Wales (1983)

Elvers, I., *Our Flora in Colour/ Var Flora i Farg*, Norstedts (1991)

Faegri, K. and Iversen, J., *Which Plant? Identification Keys for the Northwest European Pollen Flora*, Wiley

Fitter, Richard, Fitter, Alastair and Blamey, Marjorie, *The Wild Flowers of Britain and Northern Europe*, Harper Collins (1985)

Forey, P., *The Pocket Guide to Wild Flowers of the British Isles and Northern Europe*, Dragon's World (1992); *Wild Flowers of the British Isles and Northern Europe*, Dragon's World (1991)

Frohne, D. and Pfander, H. J., *A Colour Atlas of Poisonous Plants*, Manson (1984)

Gibbons, Bob and Brough, Peter, *The Hamlyn Photographic Guide to the Wild Flowers of Britain and Northern Europe*, Hamlyn (1992)

Gjaerevoll, O., *Maps of Distribution of Norwegian Vascular Plants, Vol 2 Alpine Plants*, Tapir (1990)

Glasby, J. S., *Dictionary of Plants Containing Secondary Metabolites*, Taylor & Francis (1991)

Goody, J., *The Culture of Flowers*, CUP (1993)

Grey-Wilson, Christopher and Blamey, Marjorie, *The Alpine Flowers of Britain and Northern Europe*, Harper Collins (1986)

Hayward, John, *A New Key to Wild Flowers*, CUP (1987)

Innes, C., *Wild Flowers of Spain, Vols 1–3*, Cockatrice (1987)

Jackson, B. P., and Snowdon, D. W., *Atlas of Microscopy of Medicinal Plants, Culinary Herbs and Spices*, Belhaven (1990)

Jalas, Jaako and Suominen, Julia, *Atlas Flora Europaeae, Vols 1–3*, CUP (1988)

Jordan, *The Practical Botanist*, Facts on File (1991)

Keble, Martin, *The New Concise British Flora* (1991)

Kent, D. H., *List of Vascular Plants of the British Isles*, BSBI (1992)

Landolt, Elias, *Our Alpine Flora – Swiss Alpine Club*, SAC (1991)

Launert, *Edible and Medicinal Plants of Britain and Northern Europe: Hamlyn Guides*, Hamlyn (1989)

Le Sueur, F., *Flora of Jersey*, Jersey Museum (1984)

Lewington, Anna, *Plants for People*, BMNH (1990)

Lipert and Podleich, *Collins Nature Guides: Wild Flowers*, Harper Collins (1994)

Mabey, Richard, *Food for Free*, Harper Collins (1989)

Mann, J., *Murder, Magic and Medicine*, OUP (1992)

Meikle, R. D., *The Flora of Cyprus, Vols 1–2*, Kew (1977, 1985)

Nylen, B., *Nordic Flora/Nordens Flora*, Norstedts (1992)

Parish/Parish, *Wild Flowers – A Photographic Guide*, Dovecote (1989)

Perring, *RSNC Guide to British Wild Flowers*, Hamlyn (1989)

Perring and Farrell, *British Red Data Book 1: Vascular Plants*, RSNC (1983)

Perring, F. H. and Walters, Stuart M., *Atlas of the British Flora*, BSBI (1990); *The Macmillan Field Guide to British Wildflowers*, Macmillan (1989)

Phillips, R., *Wild Flowers of Britain*, Pan (1977)

Phillips, R. and Foy, N., *Herbs – How to Grow or Gather Herbal Plants and Use Them for Cookery, Health and Beauty*, Pan (1990)

Polunin, Oleg, *A Concise Guide to the Flowers of Britain and Europe*, OUP (1987); *Collins Photoguide to Wild Flowers of Britain and Northern Europe*, Harper Collins (1987)

Polunin, Oleg and Huxley, Anthony, *Flowers of the Mediterranean*, Chatto & Windus

Polunin, Oleg and Smythies, B. E., *Flowers of South-west Europe – A Field Guide*, OUP (1988)

Press, Bob, *Photographic Field Guide: Wild Flowers of Britain and Europe*, New Holland (1993)

Rose, Francis, *The Wild Flower Key: British Isles – NW Europe – with Keys to Plants not in Flower*, Warne (1991)

Ross, R. I., *Pocket Guide to Irish Wild Flowers*, Appletree Press (1987)

Schauer and Caspari, *A Field Guide to the Wild Flowers of Britain and Europe*, Harper Collins (1982)

Sfikas, G., *Medicinal Plants of Greece*, Efstathiadis (1985); *The Wild Flowers of Crete*, Efstathiadis (1987); *Wild Flowers of Cyprus*, Efstathiadis (1993); *Wild Flowers of Greece*, Efstathiadis (1979)

Sinclair, *The Floral Charm of Cyprus*, Interworld (1992)

Stace, Clive A., *New Flora of the British Isles*, CUP (1991)

Sutton, D., *Field Guide to the Wild Flowers of Britain and Northern Europe*, Kingfisher (1988)

Turland, N. J., Chilton, L. and Press, J. R., *Flora of the Cretan Area – Annotated Checklist and Atlas*, (1993)

Turtin, T. G., Heywood, V. H. Burges et al, *Flora Europaea, Vols 1–5*, CUP (1968–93)

Vickery, R., *Plant Lore Studies*, Sheffield AP (1984)

Webb, D. A., *An Irish Flora*, Dundalgan Press (1977)

Webb, D. and Gornall, R., *Saxifrages of Europe*, Helm (1989)

Index

The Latin names of herbs are in italic type;
bold numbers indicate colour plates.

Aaron's rod *see* Great mullein
Achillea millefolium L. **94**
Agrimonia eupatoria L. **59**
— *repens* L. **175**
Agrimony **59** 175
— scented 175
Agropyron repens (L.) Beauv. 171
Alchemilla vulgaris L. 172
Alchemilla xanthochlora Rothm **31**
Alder, common 16 19 **20** 171
Alder buckthorn 17 **65** 172 175
Alliaria officinalis Andrz. 177
Alliaria petiolata (Bieb.) Cavara et
   Grande **89**
Allium schoenoprasum L. **119**
— *ursinum* L. **82**
Alnus glutinosa (L.) Gaertner **20**
Alpenrose **123** 180
Althaea officinalis L. **102**
Althaea rosea (L.) Cav. 178
Angelica archangelica L. 178
— *sylvestris* L. **93**
Angelica, garden 178
— wild 18 **93** 178
Anthemis nobilis L. 177
Anthoxanthum odoratum L. **7**
Anthyllis vulneraria L. **45**
Apple mint *see* Round-leaved
   mint
Arctium minus (Hill) Bernh, 180
— *pubens* Bab. **121**
Aristolochia clematitis L. **28**
Arnica 19 **43** 173
Arnica montana L. **43**
Artemisia absinthium L. **27**
— *vulgaris* L. **6**
Ash **22** 171
Asperula odorata L. 177

Asplenium scolopendrium L. 170
Austrian pine 170

Ballota nigra L. **103**
Basil, wild **106**
Bay 19 **64** 175
Bellis perennis L. **85**
Bermuda grass 171
Betula pendula Roth. 171
— *pubescens* Ehrh. **19**
Bilberry **118** 178 180
Bindweed, great **81** 177
Birch, downy 17 19 **19** 171
— silver 171
Birthwort **28** 172
Bistort 16 **111** 179
Biting stonecrop **34** 173
Bittersweet **136** 181
Black horehound **103** 178
— mustard 174
Blackthorn *see* Sloe
Blessed thistle 18 **56** 175
Bogbean **95** 179
Boneset *see* Hemp agrimony
Borage 17 **137** 181
Borago officinalis L. **137**
Bouncing bet *see* Soapwort
Bramble 16 **79** 177
Brassica nigra (L.) Koch 174
Briar *see* Dog-rose
Broad-leaved lavender 182
Broom **46** 173
Bryonia cretica L. *subsp. dioica*
   (Jacq.) Tutin **67**
— *dioica* Jacq. 176
Bryony, white 19 **67** 176
Buckthorn, alder 17 **65** 176
   180

— common 21 **24** 172 175
— sea **17** 19 171
Burdock, lesser 19 **121** 180
Butterbur 174

Calluna vulgaris (L.) Hull **117**
Caltha palustris L. **39**
Calystegia sepium (L.) R.Br. **81**
Cammock *see* Spiny rest-harrow
— creeping 179
Camomile 177
— wild **86** 177
Canadian fleabane **72** 175 176
Capsella bursa-pastoris (L.)
    Medicus **88**
Cardamine pratensis L. **132**
Carrot, wild 19 **71** 176
Celandine, greater **40** 173
— lesser **38** 173
Centaurea montana L. **134**
Centaurium erythraea Rafn. **112**
— *umbellatum auct.* 179
Centaury, common 18 **112** 179
Centranthus angustifolius (Mill.) DC
    180
— *ruber* (L.) DC **120**
Chamomilla recutita (L.) Rauschert
    86
Charlock 18 19 **48** 174
Cheiranthus cheiri L. **42**
Chelidonium majus L. **40**
Cherry laurel 175
Chicory 18 **140** 181
Chives **119** 180
Chrysanthemum parthenium (L.)
    Bernh. 177
— *vulgare* (L.) Bernh. 174
Cichorium intybus L. **140**
Cinquefoil, creeping **37** 173
Cistus ladanifer L. **80**
Clary **107** 179
— meadow **108** 179
Cleareye *see* Clary
Clinopodium vulgare **106**
Cloves 19
Club-moss 3
Cnicus benedictus L. **56**
Cocklebur *see* Agrimony
Colt's-foot 17 **52** 174
Comfrey, common 181

— rough **133** 181
Common alder 16 19 **20** 171
— buckthorn 17 **24** 172 175
— centaury 18 **112** 179
— comfrey 181
— heather *see* Ling
— juniper **14** 170
— lady's-mantle **31** 172
— mallow 19 **114** 178 179
— mullein **62** 175
— nettle **8** 170
— polypody **9** 170
— poppy **124** 180
— ragwort **50** 174
— sorrel **2** 17 19 169
Convolvulus sepium L. 177
Conyza canadensis (L.) Cronq. **72**
Cornflower, perennial **134** 181
Cotton lavender 18 **54** 174
Couchgrass **16** 171
Coughweed *see* Coltsfoot
Cow parsnip *see* Hogweed
Cowberry **96** 178 180
Cowslip 17 **47** 174
Crataegus laevigata (Poiret) DC
    176
— *monogyna* Jacq. **76**
Creeping cinquefoil **37** 173
Cress, small-leaved 177
Crithmum maritimum L. **26**
Cuckoo's meat *see* Wood sorrel
Cyclamen 3
Cynodon dactylon (L.) Pers. 171
Cytisus scoparius (L.) Link **46**

Daisy 17 19 **85** 177
Dandelion 18 **55** 174
Daucus carota L. **71**
Dead-nettle, white **75** 176
Digitalis purpurea **115**
Dipsacus fullonum L. **129**
— *sativus* (L.) Honck. 181
— *sylvestris* Huds. 181
Dog-rose 19 **92** 178
Dog's-mercury 17 **23** 171
Downy birch 17 19 **19** 171
Dryopteris filix-mas (L.) Schott
    11
Durmast oak *see* Sessile oak
Dwarf elder 176

Eglantine *see* Dog-rose
Elder **68** 176
Elder, dwarf 176
— grape 176
— red-berried 176
Elecampane **44** 177
Elymus repens (L.) Gould **16**
Elytrigia repens (L.) Nevski 171
Equisteum arvense L. **12**
Erigeron canadensis L. 176
Euonymus europaeus L. **66**
Eupatorium cannabinum L. **101**

False helleborine 175
Fennel 18 19 **30** 176
Fennel, sea *see* Rock samphire
— sweet 172
Fern, lady 170
— male 170
Feverfew 18 **87** 177
Five-leaved grass *see* Creeping
  cinquefoil
Ficaria ranunculoides Roth. 173
Filipendula ulmaria (L.) Maxim.
  63
Flag, yellow **41** 173
Flannel plant *see* Verbascum
Fleabane, Canadian **72** 175
  176
Foalswort *see* Coltsfoot
Foeniculum vulgare Miller **30**
Foxglove **115**
Fragaria vesca L. **78**
Frangula alnus Miller **65**
Fraxinus excelsior L. **22**
Fuller's herb *see* Soapwort
Fumaria officinalis L. **113**
Fumitory 20 **113** 179

Galium odoratum (L.) Scop.
  84
— *verum* L. **29**
Garden heliotrope *see* Valerian
— sorrel 169
— thyme 18 **98** 178
Garlic mustard **89** 177
Gentian, large yellow 18 **61**
  175
Gentiana lutea L. **61**
Geranium robertianum L. 110

Germander speedwell **139** 179
  181
Geum urbanum L. **60**
Glasswort **18** 171
Glechoma hederacea L. **141**
Glycyrrhiza glabra L. **131**
Goldenrod 17 **51** 174
Grape elder 176
Gravelroot *see* Hemp agrimony
Great bindweed **81** 177
Great mullein **62** 175
Greater celandine **40** 173
Ground ivy **141** 182
Guelder rose **83** 177
Gum cistus **80** 177

Hart's-tongue **10** 170
Hawkweed, mouse-ear **57**
  175
Hawthorn 17 **76** 176
Heartease **135** 181
Heather, common *see* Ling
Hedge garlic *see* Garlic mustard
Helleborine, false 175
Hemlock 17
Hemp agrimony **101** 178
Heracleum sphondylium L. **70**
Herb bennet **60** 175
— of grace *see* Rue
— Robert **110** 179
Hieracium pilosella L. **57**
Hippophae rhamnoides L. **17**
Hogweed **70** 176
Holy thistle *see* Blessed thistle
Hops **25** 172
Horehound, white 18 **74** 176
Horsetail **12** 18 170
Humulus lupulus L. **25**
Hypericum perforatum L. **49**
Hyssopus officinalis L. **144**

Inula helenium L. **44**
Iris pseudacorus L. **41**
Ivy 182
Ivy, ground **141** 182

Jack-by-the-hedge *see* Garlic
  mustard
Juniper, common **14** 170
— prickly **13** 170

Juniperus communis L. **14**
— *oxycedrus* L. **13**

Kidney vetch **45** 173
Knotgrass 18 **73** 176

Lady's-mantle, common **31** 172
Lady's bedstraw **29** 172
— -smock **132** 181
Lady fern 170
Lamium album L. **75**
Large-leaved lime 19 **33** 172
Large yellow gentian 18 **61** 175
Laurel, cherry 175
Laurus nobilis L. **64**
Lavandula angustifolia Miller *subsp. angustifolia* **142**
— latifolia DC 182
— vera DC 182
Lavender **142** 182
Lavender, broad-leaved 182
— cotton 18 **54** 174
Lemon verbena 180
Leonurus cardiaca L. **104**
Leopard's bane *see* Arnica
Lesser burdock **19** 121 180
— celandine **38** 173
— periwinkle **138** 181
Lily-of-the-valley 177
Lime, large-leaved 19 **33** 172
— small-leaved 172
Ling 20 **117** 180
Lippia citriodora L. 180
Liquorice **131** 181
Loosestrife, purple **122** 180
Lythrum salicaria L. **122**

Male fern **11** 170
Mallards *see* Marsh mallow
Mallow, common 19 **114** 178 179
— marsh 17 **102** 178
Malva sylvestris L. **114**
Marigold, marsh **39** 173
Maritime pine 170
Marjoram, wild **105** 179
Marrubium vulgare L. **74**
Marsh mallow 17 **102** 178
— marigold **39** 173

— trefoil *see* Bogbean
Masterwort 19 **69** 176
Matricaria perforata Mérat 177
— *recutita* L. 177
May *see* Hawthorn
Mayweed, scentless 177
Meadow bittercress *see* Lady's smock
— clary **108** 179
Meadowsweet 16 **63** 175
Melilot, ribbed **58** 175
Melitotus alba Med. 175
— *altissina* Thuill. 175
— *officinalis* (L.) Pallas **58**
Mentha aquatica L. **128**
— × *piperita* L. 181
— *rotundifolia* auct. 181
— *suaveolens* Ehrh. **127**
Menyanthes trifoliata L. **95**
Mercurialis perennis L. **23**
Milfoil *see* Yarrow
Milk thistle 175
Mint, apple *see* Round-leaved mint
— round-leaved **127** 181
— water **128** 181
Monk's rhubarb **1** 17 169
Motherwort 20 **104** 178
Mouse-ear hawkweed **57** 175
Mountain tobacco *see* Arnica
Mugwort **6** 169
Mugwort, alpine 3
Mullein, great **62** 175
Mustard, black 174
— white 174

Narrow-leaved thyme 179
Nasturtium officinale R. Br. **90**
Nerium oleander L. 175
Nettle, common **8** 170

Oak 171
— durmast 171
— sessile **21** 171
Oleander 175
Ononis repens L. 179
Oregano *see* Marjoram
Origanum majorana L. 179
— *vulgare* L. **105**
Oxalis acetosella L. **97**

Papaver argemone L. 180
— *dubium* L. 180
— *rhoeas* L. **124**
Parietaria diffusa Mert. et Koch **4**
— *judaica* L. 169
— *ramiflora* Moench 169
Pelargonium 179
Pellitory-of-the-wall **4** 169
Pepper, water- **3** 169
Peppermint 181
Perennial cornflower **134** 181
Perforate St John's-wort 19 **49** 174
Periwinkle, lesser **138** 181
Petasites hybridus (L.) Gaertn. 174
Peucedanum ostruthium (L.) Koch **69**
Phyllitis scolopendrium (L.) Newman **10**
Pilewort *see* Lesser celandine
Pine, Austrian 170
— maritime 170
— Scots **15** 19 170
— stone 170
Pinus nigra Arn. 170
— *pinaster* Aiton 170
— *pinea* L. 170
— *sylvestris* L. **15**
Pistacia terebinthus L. **125**
— *vera* L. 180
Pistacio-tree 180
Plantago lanceolata L. **5**
— *major* L. 169
— *media* L. 169
Plantain, hoary 169
— ratstail or great 169
— ribwort **5** 17 169
Polygonum aviculare L. **73**
— *bistorta* L. **111**
— *hydropiper* L. **3**
Polypodium vulgare L. **9**
Polypody, common **9** 170
Poppy, common **124** 180
— long-headed 180
— prickly-headed 180
Potentilla anserina L. **36**
— *erecta* (L.) Rauschel **35**
Potentilla reptans L. **37**
— *sterilis* (L.) Garcke 177
— *tormentilla* Stokes 173

Poterium sanguisorba L. 180
Prickly-headed poppy 180
Prickly juniper **13** 170
Primula elatior (L.) Hill 174
— *officinalis* (L.) Hill 174
— *veris* L. **47**
Prunus laurocerasus L. 175
— *spinosa* L. **77**
Purple loosestrife **122** 180

Quercus petraea (Mattuschka) Lieblein **21**
— *robur* L. 171

Radish, wild 174
Ragwort, common **50** 174
Ramsons 19 **82** 177
Ranunculus ficaria L. 38
Raphanus raphanistrum L. 174
Red valerian **120** 180
Rhamnus catharticus L. **24**
— *frangula* L. 175
Rhododendron ferrugineum L. **123**
— *hirsutum* L. 180
Rhubarb, monk's **1** 17 169
— wild **1** 17 169
Ribbed melilot **58** 175
Ribwort plantain **5** 17 169
Rock samphire **26** 172
Rosa canina L. **92**
Rose, guelder **83** 177
Rosemary 20 **130** 181
Rosmarinus officinalis L. **130**
Rough comfrey **133** 181
Round-leaved mint **127** 181
Rubus fruticosus L. **79**
Rue 17 **32** 172
Rumex acetosa L. **2**
— *alpinus* L. **1**
— *rugosus* Campd. 169
Ruta graveolens L. **32**
— *hortensis* Mill 172

Sage 18 **143** 182
Sage, meadow **108** 179
St John's-wort, perforate 19 **49** 174
Salad burnet **116** 180
Salicornia europaea L. **18**
Saltwort *see* Glasswort

Salvia officinalis L. **143**
— *pratensis* L. **108**
— *sclarea* L. **107**
Sambucus ebulus L. 176
— *nigra* L. **68**
— *racemosa* L. 176
Samphire, rock **26** 172
Sanguisorba minor Scop. **116**
Santolina chamaecyparissus L. **54**
Saponaria officinalis L. **100**
Sarothamnus scoparius (L.) Wimm.
  173
Satureia hortensis L. 178
— *montana* L. **91**
Savory, summer 178
— winter **91** 178
Scentless mayweed 177
Scots pine **15** 19 170
Sea buckthorn **17** 19 171
Sedum acre L. **34**
Senecio jacobaea L. **50**
Sessile oak **21** 171
Shepherd's-purse **88** 177
Silver birch 171
Siverweed **36** 173
Silybum marianum (L.) Gaertn.
  175
Sinapis alba L. 174
— *arvensis* L. **48**
Sloe **77** 176
Small-leaved cress 177
— lime 172
Snake-weed *see* Bistort
Soapwort 17 19 **100** 178
Solanum dulcamara L. **136**
Solidago *see* Goldenrod
Solidago virgaurea L. **51**
Sorrel, common **2** 17 19 169
— garden 169
— wood **97** 178
Speedwell, germander **139** 179
  181
Spindle **66** 175
Spiraea ulmaria L. 175
Stinging nettle *see* Common
  nettle
Stone pine 170
Stonecrop, biting **34** 173
Strawberry, wild **78** 176
Summer savory 178

Sun-rose *see* Gum cistus
Sweet fennel 172
— vernal grass **7** 170
Symphytum asperum Lepechin
  133
— *officinale* L. 181

Tanacetum parthenium (L.) Schultz
  Bip. **87**
— *vulgare* L. **53**
Tansy **53** 174
Taraxacum vulgare Schrank **55**
Teasel, wild 20 **129** 181
Thistle, blessed 18 **56** 175
— holy *see* Blessed thistle
— milk 175
Thyme, garden 18 **98** 178
— narrow-leaved 179
— wild 18 **109** 179
Thymus × *citriodorus* (Pers.)
  Schreb 178
— *pulegioides* L. **109**
— *serpyllum* L. 179
— *vulgaris* L. **98**
Tilia cordata Mill. 173
— *platyphyllos* Scop. **33**
— × *vulgaris* Hayne 173
Tormentil 16 **35** 173
Turpentine tree **125** 180
Tussilago farfara L. **52**

Urtica dioica L. **8**

Vaccinium myrtillus L. **118**
— *vitis-idaea* L. **96**
Valerian 18 **99** 178
Valerian, red **120** 180
Valeriana officinalis auct. *non* L.
  178
— *repens* Host **99**
Veratrum album L. 175
Verbascum densiflorum Bertol 175
— *phlomoides* L. 175
— *thapsus* L. **62**
Verbena officinalis L. **126**
Vernal grass, sweet **7** 170
Veronica chamaedrys L. **139**
Vervain **126** 180
Vetch, kidney **45** 173
Viburnum opulus L. **83**

Vinca minor L. **138**
Viola tricolor L. **135**

Wall pellitory *see* Pellitory-of-
   the-Wall
Wallflower **42** 173
Wallpepper *see* Stonecrop
Water mint **128** 181
— -pepper **3** 169
Watercress 19 **90** 177
White bryony **67** 176
— dead-nettle **75** 176
— horehound 18 **74** 176
— mustard *see* Charlock
Whitethorn *see* Hawthorn
Wild angelica 18 **93** 178
— basil **106**

— camomile **86** 177
— carrot 19 **71** 176
— marjoram **105** 179
— mustard *see* Charlock
— radish 174
— rhubarb *see* Monk's rhubarb
— shamrock *see* Wood sorrel
— strawberry **78** 176
— teasel 20 **129** 181
— thyme 18 **109** 179
Winter savory **91** 178
Wood sorrel **97** 178
Woodruff **84** 177
Wormwood 18 **27** 169 172 182

Yarrow 19 **94** 178
Yellow flag **41** 173